Walls and Bridges

Walls and Bridges

Bodmin to Broadmoor:
A Journey Working in Mental Health

Paul Deacon

NAPICU International Press
East Kilbride

© Paul Deacon, 2019

First published in 2019 by NAPICU International Press, an imprint of the National Association of Psychiatric Intensive Care and Low Secure Units (NAPICU), 60 Nasmyth Avenue, East Kilbride G75 0QR, UK. http://napicu.org.uk

A CIP catalogue record for this book is available from the British Library.

ISBN: 978-1-9161192-0-8 (Paperback)
ISBN: 978-1-9161192-1-5 (ePub)
ISBN: 978-1-9161192-2-2 (Mobi)

Book layout and design by Clare Brayshaw

Cover design by Jon Deacon

Typeset and printed by:
York Publishing Services Ltd
64 Hallfield Road
Layerthorpe
York YO31 7ZQ

Tel: 01904 431213

Website: www.yps-publishing.co.uk

This book is dedicated to:

My dad, Cyril Deacon – Registered Mental Nurse
My mum, Ruth Deacon – Qualified Nursery Nurse
My two sons and twin daughters

Acknowledgements

I would like to express a big thank you to Debra Jeremiah, a lady I met for the first time and spent a good two hours in discussion with on our first meeting. When we first met I didn't really know where this was all going; it certainly wasn't about writing a book. We had met for a meeting which ended up being cancelled due to ward staff commitments. Without her initial input none of this would have happened. She informed me that everyone had a book in them, and that I certainly had a story to tell. Thank you for your words of wisdom and for demonstrating such faith in my abilities that I actually began to believe I could do it.

Thank you to those really close to me. All of you were so brilliant to work with and be with over the years. Your determination, passion, humour and dedication will never be forgotten. You are the most intelligent, witty, funny and understanding people I have ever met.

More specifically, I would like to thank the following people for the support and encouragement that they have given me over the years; there are so many apologies if I have left anyone out. All of these people and more have left an impression on me that has affected my views on so many things in life.

My four children, Mum and Dad, Brother Jon Deacon (who designed the front cover, and formulated all the photographs).

St Lawrence's Hospital mentors: the late Steve Davis, Dave Bowden, Andy Jago, Mark Steer, Peter Marlow, Alick Barrie, Dave Tyrrell, the late Roy Blake, Rodney Warne, Harold Vanderwolfe, Kevin Hennely, the late Sister Irene Clancy, the late Eddie Campbell, Lindsay Parkin, Heather Pritchard, Clive Denny, Carolyn Tothill, Mark Milton, Michaela Burt, Debbie Waters, Sue Jago, Lesley Maynard-Beresford, Dr Neil Owen, Glynis Dean, Pat Broderick, the late Dr Nick Kitson, the late Les Gerkin, Dora Heaton, Magdalene, Linda Hennel, Switchboard, Sarah Fisher, the late Roger Mitchell, Paul Endean, Dave Burghes, Ian Ringer, Elaine Clack, Alan Miles, Dr Mike Badve, Iain Knox, Jonnie Morris, Helen Lynch.

Broadmoor Hospital mentors: Chris Hartwell, Mark Watts, Pat McKee, George Tinsley, Mick Harry, Brian de-Hooten, Mick and Carol Pither, Tim Brett, Dave Hunt, Jim Lowrie, Jim Smith, Jimmy Noakes, Dawn Hodges, Dr Clive Meaux, Ivan Dawson.

National colleagues: The entire NAPICU executive team, Northern Networks, Malcolm Rae OBE, all the staff at Broadmoor Hospital, the staff at the Liverpool Lennon Airport, Bob Paxman of Talking 2 Minds, Clive Travis, The Royal College of Psychiatrists (AIMS-PICU).

Social circle: John Beer, Jeanette Brown, Anthony Doyle, Mandy Hearn, Rose Jennings, Dave Searle, Anna Sharp, Rhydian Thomas, Ryan Trelevan, Sue Webb, John Young, Maggie Williams, Paul Hearn, Mike Gough, Paddy Doyle, Michael Cocks, Nigel Dawe, Paul Hildersley.

Contents

Prologue

And in the Beginning there was Nothing

Nothing has ever been straight forward in my life, and writing this book is no exception. You know how it is when you really get into something: you tend to throw yourself right into it. When you start writing and it happens to be your own story, the whole memory thing can be more than a bit of a worry. All those memories that became activated once I had connected my jump leads. At times I found myself doubting that I had been in certain places and kept having to confirm events. Writing has been so satisfying and very therapeutic, if humbling and harrowing at times. Each time I opened my laptop I would find myself ready to enter into different chapters that I had already drafted out. I don't really think like a book, it's more a question of new bursts of ideas invading my head, pictures, lists and charts. I would channel new ideas during my nightly sleep walk, having been a pacer most of my life. The years to come would be like piecing together a jigsaw.

I would sit there clicking onto a sentence, paragraph, deleting it, restoring it, deleting it again, and then restoring. How many times have I re-read a sentence and thought, 'That's not what I meant' and deleted it? Would I write one page per day over 365 days or just go with the flow? When I spoke to real writers who I contacted through various routes, they were really honest with me; they had found every excuse in the world not to write. For the next three years my entire house would be plastered from wall to wall with flip chart paper, Post-its, photographs, slides, negatives, portfolios, diaries, telephone numbers, address books, correspondence, certificates, emails, letters, videos, DVDs, references, reflective diaries, cards, press coverage, and boxes of files containing documentation of the times. My times, their times, and our times.

I hadn't really thought of writer's block until I started writing this book. To be honest I wasn't aware that it existed, but over the next thirty-six months the blocks became very familiar to me. Writing either a book or an assignment, can be such a wonderful way of making sense of your life-career. I would wake up in the early hours of the morning and say 'Yes!' and put some nugget down on paper which was always beside me everywhere I went. I would write in hotels, on trains, as a passenger in a car, on a plane, in the garden, in the toilet, a waiting room, on the beach, Bodmin Moor, whilst cooking, just about everywhere. I had a note pad and continued to write what came into my head at that precise moment. At times I would end up writing nothing at all.

The more I wrote, the more time I had to reflect and come back to it. The whole thing at times would be bizarre, as you would just hear the words flowing. Everything was right there staring at me straight in the face. I learnt that you don't have to be a writer to write. It's about getting all your thoughts down despite how disorganised it may appear at first. There is no right way of doing it. What matters is the process of how one feels.

This book is about my journey, vision and hope. A journey as a young lad who grew up in the 70s and ended up working for forty-one years in mental health. I worked in various roles throughout my career, starting off as a nursing assistant, progressing through healthcare assistant, lead healthcare assistant, student nurse, staff nurse, liaison nurse, charge nurse, and finally ward manager. There are many stories and events to tell, some sad, some hilarious. However, even now some are still so very painful to recall. In fact, there have been some very unpleasant and tough moments in my career, things which a lot of nurses out there will be able to relate to. You are exposed to people's personal tragedies and abuse, as well as horrific crimes that people have committed whilst being mentally unwell. I have without a doubt nursed deeply troubled, challenging and lonely people. A mental health professional can at times be torn between compassion, anger, sorrow and empathy.

As I said, this happens to be my own story as well as my first time writing, and I was advised not to lose any passion and to just go for it and say it as it is. Having taken the plunge to start the project, I met up with ex colleagues from Broadmoor Hospital and St Lawrence's Hospital, and found myself thinking about everything that we had discussed. My colleagues' past and present were available to me during my writing process, they shared insights, personal experiences and stories of inspiration. Without taking too long to think about the events for this book we would document the places and times and went with it. Having delved into my past so recently, a lot of what we talked about was familiar territory, at times emotional. These conversations certainly unpicked locks, reopening long sealed memories for all of us.

For myself and others, our experience working at Broadmoor Hospital could never be wholly captured, because my time spent working there was so valuable and vast. I could end up writing volumes just about Broadmoor. It has to be said that no project like this is achieved without support and guidance from other people. I have spent so many hours with colleagues, friends and family, checking recollections and events. I have many people to thank, and stand proud in acknowledging their help, guidance and enthusiasm.

It sounds crazy, but sitting here now and rereading the when, what and wherefore, I wonder if I've captured it all exactly as it happened. However, memory is a strange thing and since writing I have realised that people's memories of the same event can be so different. Therefore, what follows is only my memory of what I experienced in my life at the time. It may not be precisely how it was, but I can say that this is how it seemed to me at the time.

'Walls and Bridges' you may ask? The Wall represents the obstacles that became a barrier throughout my youth and my career, and there were a few. The Bridges became the solutions: helping hands, support, mentorship, guidance, signposting and encouragement. My whole career has consisted of driving forward and jumping through those hoops.

I recommend that all those who are thinking of enrolling in mental health nursing should start a portfolio of your own journey; mine has not only kept me up to date, it has also become a time line for this book. Certificates, conferences, reflection notes, letters, plaudits, press coverage, emails, photographs, the list is endless. It would make sense to me that people working in the caring profession should have to provide reliable evidence that they are keeping themselves up to date. The culture of this kind of work is changing all the time. Many years ago, people tended to remain in the same area of the health service. Their roles remained quite static and they were able to maintain effectiveness in their roles. However, the situation is so different now. People are changing roles within the healthcare profession, the boundaries and spheres of practice are changing all the time, and at a sometimes alarmingly fast pace. Working in mental health is certainly not a career for everyone, so choices have to be made.

I have mentored so many students over the years – vocational candidates, cadets, apprentices and healthcare assistants – that I have lost count. I have always said to myself that what my family, colleagues and mentors had given me throughout the years I would give back to others. This also includes friends outside of the National Health Service (NHS). My forty-one years working in mental health have been challenging to say the least and have made me a stronger person all round. I officially retired from my ward manager's post working on a psychiatric intensive care unit (PICU) based in Cornwall in April 2012.

Writing has really made me reflect on all the different psychiatric hospitals I have worked in, my roles, projects, academic courses and presentations I have been involved in over the years, whether I have been delivering them or enrolled myself. How on earth can all this be achieved with your family, full-time job, all that is thrown at you in life. There are many things to do before going to work every morning. Showering, brushing your teeth, shaving, feeding the children, changing around the kids' car seats for child minders, nappy change times three, feeding yourself (or not), finding the car keys, and dashing out the door.

A key note throughout this book is the fact that music became a diary for me and has helped me with events throughout my life; whether it was rock, pop, punk, new wave, progressive or easy listening. I would become a genuine music fanatic. What would keep me focused one hundred percent was just this. The one thing I do know about myself is the fact that my music knowledge is not flawed in any way; this is a massive pastime for me. Different songs take me back to a specific memory; it's like having a musical encyclopedia inside my mind. Each track is special and means something to me. I have always had energy and at times people would say to me 'slow down you get involved in so much', sometimes too much. I feel that I am a completer, however, at times found this proved difficult in the NHS due to the volume of different projects that came along with very short deadlines.

I have been privileged enough to meet many people over the years, whether I have nursed them, worked with them, just met them, or they have had some connection with the mental health services. They are directors, consultants, doctors, pharmacists, staff nurses, enrolled nurses, nursing assistants, domestics, ward clerks, healthcare assistants, psychologists, occupational therapists, art therapists, holistic therapists, cadets, apprentices, tutors, lead nurses, nurse consultants, secretaries and social workers.

Then there were those that were in the public limelight: Diana, the Princes of Wales, Jo Brand, Camilla, Duchess of Cornwall, Barbara Windsor and Frank Bruno. I really doubt if I had not been in this line of work that I would not have had the opportunity to meet, listen, and talk to all these people. I don't mention these names as boasts, but rather as evidence of how privileged I have been throughout my entire nursing career.

According to my family and close friends, I was always a bit of a handful. Eventually I grew extremely tired of my early aimless life. Later on I got more serious. The fact is that life never quite goes according to plan. Everyone has set backs. No one can be unaffected by the things that happen to them. It's the nature of life and you just have to get over them. Just like anyone else, my journey has been a turbulence of days that have rolled into each other, some with direction and others without. I am more of a private person than most people realise. There are times when you need light and others when you need some shade. This book was the result of the discontented feelings arising from a particularly difficult four years of my life, after the turbulence of a divorce. As I began to reposition myself both socially and at work, pleasure and graft were high on the agenda. I finally seemed to recognise the folly of repeated 'Groundhog Day' cycles in so many areas of my life. It was time to do something about it.

After time, I would reflect on decisions made in the past and come to see that things change, goalposts move. I knew that I had to move on from all of this and I did. Various things we do in life are driven by pure emotion rather than practicality. Sometimes we can have a simplistic view on life and the way we treat people close to us, and vice versa. When you're in the middle of any turbulence, or curve balls continually come your way, you're not always able to express yourself. Why? Because you are too busy dealing with it. It's only when you come out of the other side that you start to have some perception of the way it has affected you, or not.

Chapter One

The Early Days

I'm not totally convinced that everyone out there views their teenage youth with the same passion as I do, despite the not so good times. I guess this displays the true strength of my family. My daily family atmosphere had everything to do with who I am today, I stand proud. I was born in Plymouth, Devon, England in 1957 and came from a family of four, two brothers and my dear little sister. I had a fairly happy upbringing and came from a very creative family; I have learnt so much from them all. It's not until you look around that you realise how lucky you are. My Dad and my two brothers were very clever with their hands. By this I mean they had a talent for graphic design, oil painting, calligraphy, moulding models from clay, and designing scenes. By using their hands to create things, they shared a lot of great hours together. I don't ever remember them losing this artistic side.

At the time I excelled at very little, except perhaps knowing my music, and sticking cut-outs from catalogues onto paper to create a picture. I would try making models from toilet rolls and cereal boxes, but they would all fall apart. Most of the time we had to use our own creativity to think of something to do, or else not do anything at all. One of the benefits of having siblings is that you have a shared history of growing up. You are able to appreciate their points of view. Siblings help you with the highs and the lows, they act as a sounding board, or a punch bag depending on which way it goes!

It's bizarre how we remember scenes from our childhood at random. Of course the first few years are blank, although I can remember the word 'sweets', playing 'What's the time Mr Wolfe', having scraped knees, being told every five minutes to 'Stop my nonsense' and being informed by my Mum that Brussels sprouts were a luxury. Birthdays were celebrated with sponge cakes and ice cream with just the family, not with twenty friends.

My Mum had a little radio that she called a wireless that she would take all around the house with her. The radio is an incredibly effective vehicle for people. It is a pipeline into homes and hearts.

In the front room we had a record player on which you could load up to six records at once and listen as they were lowered down and played through in turn. However, most of my memories are hazy-fleeting pictures that don't always make a lot of sense. I didn't know an awful lot about Plymouth back then except for the Barbican, the Hoe, Eddystone Lighthouse, and the opening of the Tamar Bridge. We never went abroad on holidays, we just couldn't afford it. Neither could anyone else we mingled with. Yet we did manage to have great holidays in England. My grandparents played a significant part in our early years on both sides of the family as in they were always present.

I do remember the silences around the house with little explanation as to why. I would discover in later years that I was being spared the news that something dreadful had happened to someone that we had known. Or I was being sheltered from any neighbourhood gossip. Being shielded from these things became more problematic in years to come, as when a tragedy did come my way, it seemed to strike me like a bolt of lightning. Protect your kids yes, but not over the top.

The one thing I do remember is hating my first infant school. I did everything possible not to attend. Wouldn't you if you were continuously singled out, informed that you're a waster, loser and an idiot. I can still hear the teachers voice now, 'You've only been here five minutes and you have clearly demonstrated that you are incapable of listening and learning'. I received detention for mixing up two words when I recited a poem with simple illustrations that we had to learn off by heart. There were no ambiguities or grey areas, you were either word perfect or you were in big trouble.

No wonder I spent the first ten years of my life suffering from migraines. I yelled my head off every time I was dropped off in the playground where there was always mischievous energy and boisterousness going on. There would be kids running everywhere. Piggyback fights would take place where punches were thrown to try and knock the other person off their mate's back. Other kids were wailing and clinging on to their parents. We all wore pudding basin haircuts, fashionable – not! I had the imprint of the iron fence bars engrained on my forehead. I could be heard yelling from Hyde Park School right over to the other side of Plymouth Argyle Football Stadium. Some people thought it was a plane coming out of the sky!

The school meals made me feel sick to my stomach; sitting at long tables with twelve other kids that you disliked. The noise of cutlery clanking away and teachers looking over you like prison wardens making sure you ate the last powdery lump of your rice pudding. You could turn the jug upside down without a drop coming out. I couldn't wait for break time when you were given a half pint bottle of warm congealed milk. It was always the boys' job to carry the milk crates into the classroom each day. Most of my meals were dropped to the floorboards and smudged into the cracks with my shoes (which incidentally had left and right written on them in bold red ink). Mind you, it certainly helped me before crossing any roads. I would have to look down at my shoes first before I looked right, left, then right again. What a performance that was.

During my time at this infant school, I remember eating school dinners in a hall which smelt of damp concrete. The strict dinner ladies would not let you outside until you had made a reasonable effort at consuming their sloppy unappetising meals. There was no choice; thick lumpy custard was a regular pudding on their so-called menu. Would you honestly eat 'spam fritter rolls'? Wouldn't it have been fantastic if chef Jamie Oliver had been on the scene back then? I would always know where I had last sat and eaten, I would walk along the floor and bits of stale food would gush up through the floorboards – rancid! The cooks were bullies. You could hear them in the kitchen battering fish, beating eggs, and whipping cream. They were nasty with a hard no-nonsense attitude. The teachers on dinner duty would call us to the front of the dinner hall and proceed to examine our heads in search of nasty invaders, nits!

Throughout these years, we still had a school dentist who was ready to point (or chisel) out who hadn't been cleaning their teeth appropriately. Most of the fillings in my mouth were directly related to chewing gum. My jaw would ache by the time I had finished one of those brick sized packages of Wrigley's. We also had our hearing tested and received eye examinations from a school optician. Of course, none of these health checks exist in schools today, surely this is paramount? I remember the female school nurse very well, I would spend hours complaining of severe migraines in order to spend time on the couch. Migraines that didn't always exist I might add! Yes, I did have a crush on her! It was while I was at Hyde Park School that I began to recognise and get a glimpse of my future education: not that good I thought. The highlight of this school was going to the tuck shop after 3pm on a Friday and buying six pence worth of Black Jacks, Fruit Salads, Sherbet Dips, and Gobstoppers. This would be washed down with a bottle of Cherry Panda Pop. I then knew that my favourite day – Saturday – was coming around fast. I would then be able to buy either the Beano, Topper, Dandy or Beezer comics.

I can tell you that I wasn't proud of my school uniform, grey jumper and trousers, white shirt and black shoes, and as for my tie and school cap ... My uniform was disgusting; please don't mention the satchel. The one thing I do remember in the playground is hearing about the Beatles and their number one hit 'She loves you'. I had not heard the song but asked who they were. The Beatles were coming to Plymouth to play. I was to discover that the city of Liverpool was opening out and making an announcement to the whole wide world. These four young lads were going to explode within the music scene. No other band at the time had pulled off anything close in size or style to their headline grabbing fab raves. After years of touring in Hamburg and Liverpool's Cavern Club, their efforts had arrived at a sound and look that had seen them elected as figureheads of a musical phenomenon. How ironic that they were to dominate my life, music-wise, later on in life. I can remember from an early age becoming interested in music, having despised just about everything else that was on offer around me. I really wanted to live my life through music. I would walk around the house with a radio strapped to my ears.

Apart from school, life was pretty normal. As a young child our role was pretty straightforward, we were just an ordinary family really. Sunday tea time I can remember clearly; it consisted of sandwiches; chicken paste or corned beef. Boy, did we eat a lot of paste in sandwiches. Puddings would be either jelly or ice cream. Maybe window cake (known as Battenberg) if you were good. The unbearable times were knowing that school was looming the next day. In fact they were gut-wrenching. After tea it was bath time with the ducks, Quirky and Quacky. The rest is a bit of a blur until we learnt that life was going to change in a big way.

Back in the late mid 60s my parents took up the offer of moving to Vancouver in British Columbia, Canada. There was a massive recruitment drive for mental health nurses at that time. Dad was offered a job after a successful interview and suddenly a whole new future loomed, a once in a lifetime opportunity. When I was informed by my parents that we were emigrating I thought this was just up the road. I couldn't work out why all my personal belongings including my metal Corgi ice cream van were being packed into a black trunk, bolted down with heavy duty locks. We weren't just going up the road at all; we were going 6000 miles away to another country, Canada! I was on the cusp of moving on to the next exciting phase of my life and would become a Vancouverite, but what about the window cake?

We travelled to Canada on a liner, the Cunard 'Franconia' which departed from Southampton; I was eight years old when we travelled. There was a big build up before departing, what with all the organising. The six day sailing journey on this magnificent liner left me physically ill with sea sickness, the sea was terribly rough. I remember six paper bags being used for vomit on the hour. We arrived in Montreal and anchored. After a day spent there we boarded the train to take us to Vancouver, it took us three days and three nights travelling through the Rockies. The views were stunning.

Living in Vancouver was a fantastic experience, and I have so many fond memories of the years that we lived and grew up there; how lucky were we. Vancouver is a beautiful scenic city that shines so bright, even when it's snowing. It's well known as an urban centre surrounded by nature, making tourism its second-largest industry. The city was very cosmopolitan. It wasn't that large a city back then, but it did look big to us, with its freeways and traffic; business people walking around. We were also surrounded by beautiful coastlines and beaches, mountains and ski slopes to the north, flat farmland to the south, and the prairies to the east. At the time, Vancouver was a very safe city to live in. It is consistently ranked in the top five most liveable cities in the world. As a young diverse city, its culture is relatively undeveloped compared to cities like New York or London. My time settling into this new way of life was spent playing in parks, swimming in lakes, attending BBQs, viewing the mountains, riding my second hand bike along trails, watching people ski down the mountain slopes, and the pleasure of the beaches and blue sea. There was a wealth of outdoor activities. All of this was within easy reach of where we now lived.

I discovered that Vancouverites were really nice people who would do anything for you. They also liked giving people their own space. I soon met new friends, which helped and distracted me from the dreaded thought of starting a new school. It was summer time and I didn't have a care in the world. Why would I? After all I was a kid in a new country. I had weeks and weeks of exploring. There was so much freedom and space, it was nothing like I was used to. The transport system was easy, what with buses and trains (and my bike). Whatever type of food you had a craving for it was here on your doorstep. Despite rainy seasons, summers were bright and cheerful and filled with colour. Most families lived in single-family homes, and there were no concrete skyscrapers.

Vancouver was a kid's city, a city to explore all-day long. Stanley Park (Vancouver's largest park) was where we had many a family outing. This often included a fish and chip supper at Lumberman's Arch, eaten on the beach whilst watching the ferries pass under the Lion's Gate Bridge on the way to Vancouver Island. Although both countries spoke the English language, we found that there were many words and expressions we had to fathom and we soon learnt the dos and don'ts. For example, the Head Teacher was the Principal, school hall–auditorium, pram–buggy, teatime – supper time, biscuits–cookies, crisps–chips and motorway–freeway.

Canada welcomed us with totem poles, the Royal Canadian Mounty Police, maple leaves, snow, pancakes with maple syrup and whipped cream. It didn't take very long to fall in love with the place, the vibe as a child was great from the very onset. To say that growing up in Vancouver had an insightful effect on my life would be an understatement.

I listened to CFUN music station which at the time was the business. Major film production studios in Vancouver turned Metro Vancouver into one of the largest film production centers in North America, earning it the film industry nickname Hollywood North. Here, they shot the *X Files*, *Stargate*, *Battlestar Galactica*, *I-Robot*, *Cat Woman*, *The A Team*, *Fringe*, *Smallville*, *Mission Impossible* and *Rumble in the Bronx* to name but a few. Vancouver held the 1986 Expo Exhibition, the 2010 winter Olympics, and the Vancouver Canucks hockey team were top of the league for four years. When Paul McCartney played to sixty-five thousand people in the British Columbia Coliseum in November 2012, most of my family were there.

During the summer holiday I ignored any conversations my parents had with me about attending my new school. The thought of buying a new pencil case, notepads and rubbers made me cringe. This went on for weeks until the summer holidays ended. I had no choice but to conform. In the first week at my new Vancouver school I picked up that this school didn't reek of disinfectant like the one back in England, the toilet paper was spongy opposed to the rough brown tracing paper we had just left behind. I looked around the classroom and observed the look of fear, panic and excitement in pupils' faces. They were all looking around to see who was confident, relaxed, and who was going to be a bit of a handful.

The classrooms were all arranged in strict rows, facing the blackboard. I only remember one class held in the auditorium when the classrooms were being redecorated. I would spend days worrying about a comment made by a girl sitting behind me in class. I must have been about eight when she insisted that if you pick your nose your head blows off! Something I have never forgotten really. Charles Dickens School was an interesting red brick building with large windows and pictures of Dickens everywhere. It had long corridors which weren't so great when you were at the wrong end and late for class.

Schools in Canada were very much like American high schools; you could understand why the film *Grease* was so popular. We were treated every three months to a Charles Dickens film, *Great Expectations* being one of them. However, I would have given anything to have missed these films and gone outside to play with my marbles, bubble gum hockey cards or my conkers. All schools in Canada were named after people, not areas. Although by this time I wasn't a great lover of learning, I felt that this school would do for now. It felt more laid back and you didn't feel hounded so much.

However, I soon discovered that many words were spelt differently and the entire curriculum was the opposite of what I had just left in England. I found this more than a struggle, so I channelled my energies into sports, ice skating, discovering music and fun. My yearly school results were dismal and I just went further back into the system. This resulted in my giving up totally on what was on offer. At the time I would aspire to simplicity; I wasn't desperately bothered by complexity. I knew every object in the Principal's office, because that's where I spent most of my time being lectured on my poor results and behaviour. I couldn't have cared less what the Principal's last verdict on me was going to be.

On my first day of school my teacher asked all the troublemakers to stand up. Eventually I stood up and the teacher asked, 'Are you a troublemaker?' I said, 'No.' The teacher asked me why I was standing and I replied, 'Well you looked pretty stupid standing there on your own.' Later, I can remember him shouting out, 'Deacon, will you stop passing notes while I am teaching?' I replied, 'I'm not passing notes Sir, I'm playing cards.' My t-shirt's logo under my uniform shirt read, 'Not conforming to your regulated standards'. Listening to authority wasn't on my list of things to do. Interestingly enough, when the Principal lost his temper with me his eyes would turn black – or was this just a dark ring around his eyes? The teachers had all been here since day one of their careers and would remain at this school for the next forty-five years in order to receive their gold watch for service with their name inscribed on it. Give me strength.

School relations began to reach an all-time low. I was the only lad in the class to receive 0% for an English test. Slightly unfair I thought, I'm sure I spelled my name right on the paper which would have given me 1%. I couldn't do basic maths, times tables, basic spelling or even tell the time. (Looking forward to the future then I would say to myself.) What was it about education and schools? Trouble was looming. In saying this, I did know my ABC 'Always Be Cool'. The one thing I did relish was the school holidays and would count the days down until the end of term.

I was always into various money-making schemes and would seek work anywhere to bring in a buck or two. The one thing I did not have was splinters in my backside from sitting around. I did a local paper round delivering the Vancouver Sun, sold ice cream in Stanley Park. I would sweep people's paths and drives for them, earning 50 cents a drive. Business would be booming when it had snowed of course. I would get around the neighbourhood by sneaking up behind cars with snow chains, grip hold of the bumper and ski from house to house. I considered this to be safer than falling down in the snow and breaking my leg, which would have affected my daily income.

I always had a wet rear end which my Mum could never work out. I would wave to those passing me by doing the same thing on the opposite side of the road. On occasions we would exchange bubble gum cards holding onto the bumper with one hand. If you missed the other card then you lost out. This was before excessive health and safety rules came into play and literally ruined all of our fun. Back then, no one was given grief for such antics, it was simply a bit of fun. Life just cannot be lived without taking risks I would say to myself, the trick is to learn how to deal with them. In the school summer holidays I became a skilled picker, collecting bucketsful of strawberries. Everyone would know what I was up to as my fingers would be scratched and stained red. I would earn a substantial amount of money doing this. I immersed myself in this activity with enthusiasm. Seeing who could pick the most strawberries gave the day a competitive element, and more cash of course. It was also a good way to spend hours in the sun and get sun tanned golden brown.

I also spent six months delivering eggs in the heart of Vancouver. I was poached from the strawberry job when a fellow worker observed the way I delivered and put me in touch with the manager of the egg deliveries. They also shelled out better money because what I was earning was a real yoke! I have to say the job was hardly stimulating and in the end it scrambled my head, so I left. Well the one thing for sure was that my talents were appreciated doing this kind of work, despite being overlooked at school. Putting my education, or lack thereof, to one side, I thoroughly relished the social side of this beautiful country and what it had to offer young people. It didn't take me long to develop a social network, which in turn gave me some fantastic memories of growing up there. Canadians are so laid back. I not only had numerous friends, but their parents would also take you in and you would all become one family. By our seventh year living in Vancouver, apart from school, I loved it. As a family, we would all be excited when a blue air mail envelope letter arrived containing all the news from our Grandparents who were still living in Plymouth.

However, this was all to come to an unexpected end through no one's fault. The news was earth shattering. I can still remember my knees buckling and the lump in my throat when we were all sat down in the living room and informed by my parents; my stomach was churning. We had all settled here and this was now our home, but it wasn't to be. We were returning to England because my grandparents were unwell. Over a period of a few months, they had all deteriorated very quickly through old age and ill health. It was a difficult call and I respected my parents for making this decision; after all we have a duty to look after our families. However, on reflection it would have been so much easier if we as kids had been informed and updated a lot earlier so that it didn't come as such a massive shock.

I had two years of schooling left to complete. I was distraught and felt that my world had been pulled apart. I said my goodbyes over the weeks to come. It was quite a life changing event, leaving a city as large as Vancouver, touching back down to base in Plymouth Devon, then Bodmin Cornwall. I was fully aware at this age that I had been disconnected from the heart of a city and tossed into the sticks. I was a teenager by now, with a broken voice and getting taller. This was to be another chapter in my life.

Chapter Two

The Teenage Years

Weeks after settling back in England my Dad was successful in being appointed to a staff nurse (mental health) post at St Lawrence's Hospital in Bodmin, Cornwall. He had previously secured a high position in Vancouver working for the Narcotic Addiction Foundation. Looking back, the management of St Lawrence's Hospital had a very good deal; my Dad was creative, inspiring, focused, well educated, and his thinking was right outside of the box for that era. I don't ever remember my Dad missing a day's work. Nursing staff would often say that he would always include so many different learning styles into his teaching, even bringing in 'George' the puppet who would interact with the staff training cohort. Another one of his ideas that comes to mind was the attaching of blood vials to homing pigeons. The pigeons would then fly off to the local general hospitals, speeding up the blood results. In later years he progressed on up within his career pathway.

We moved to Bodmin, which was a small town when we arrived in 1971. The town had lost its importance over the decades; its barracks, prison, railway and courts had all gone. The only thing that grew was the population. The old Army Barracks, Duke of Cornwall's Light Infantry (DCLI) had been occupied by the American Army during the Second World War. It was also a Russian language school for British spies during the Cold War. The town has undergone many changes in the last few decades, and has certainly grown since we arrived. Priory Café was our first stop and we all sat and drank strawberry milkshakes. They were the best ever, and far superior to Woolworths' milkshakes. It was a Wednesday, and I remember all the shops closing in the afternoon, which was normal back then.

We lived on a new housing estate in a new-built house that my parents had had to wait for a further week for before they could move in. It was called Hillside Park, and their first house after moving to England. Our spacious four-bedroom house backed onto a large garden which was very well laid out. Taking a small hop over the fence you could take a walk along a path to other new houses being built nearby. Everything we needed at the time was just there. The library, Bunts newsagents, Liptons, Dewhurst butchers, wool shops, Bricknells toy shop, and the family with Canadian accents. I knew I had to transform this move into an exciting challenge. So, instead of letting regrets about what I had lost overwhelm me, I decided to explore the area. I certainly wasn't going to lock myself up in our new house spending endless days unpacking. I would have plenty of time to put the finishing touches to my bedroom at a later stage. I left my parents to all the paperwork, finding a school for us, a doctor and so on.

Having just settled in, it appeared that everyone knew everyone's business, and everyone looked out for everyone else. It was when neighbourhood watch really worked, and resentments never lasted. Like many Cornish towns back then, they didn't really offer that much to a curious and bored teenage mind.

It wasn't long before I was enrolled at Bodmin Comprehensive School. 'Here we go again', I thought, 'another prison sentence!' On my first day, I arrived at 08.45 having just eaten a bowl of yucky Ready Brek which made you 'glow' all the way to school. In Canada we wore our own individual clothes to school, uniforms were definitely out, so back in England I really stood out from the crowd until I got myself kitted out. I remember wearing a pair of high waist flared trousers which would spread out like sails when it was windy, a bright Ben Sherman purple shirt with wing collars, and 3 inch platform 'Dave Hill' boots (Slade's trademark being a favourite band of mine). I was still limping from an ankle recently sprained just for the sake of a bit of style. For the next eighteen months I went from 5 foot 7 inches to 6 foot 2! Please take my word that all of the above were trendy at the time.

I would board a train to Plymouth to purchase boots like the ones my pop and rock idols wore on stage. I remember sales shooting through the roof. I lost a few inches in height when platforms were eventually phased out. The one thing I liked about this era was the fashion. I admired the amount of individuality and the fact that no one looked quite the same. I think I was wearing Brut 33 aftershave, or was it Old Spice? Talk about standing out in the school crowd. I had only just converted from chewing Canadian Chiclets' Classic chewing gum to the English Bazooka Joe bubble-gum which tasted like cardboard.

As fellow pupils approached me and my brothers and sister, circling around like a collie dog rounding up the sheep, I heard someone say, 'Who's that?' The reply was, 'He must be a member of the Partridge family.' I can still hear her voice to this day, she was wearing Charlie perfume; this was like Brut 33 for the girls. I then heard someone shout out, 'What do you think you are, posh?' The other kids were constantly telling me how much they loved my Canadian accent. I would reply through gritted teeth, 'I love yours as well.' This school had a uniform and it was mandatory. I was in a uniform by the end of the week; it was taken seriously by the school. There was nothing trendy about this at all.

These people would be the ones that I would start to hang around with on a daily basis. It was only a matter of days before I would be joining them singing down the corridor on route to our next lesson. Gripping bottles of Pepsi we would shout out loud, 'Hey you with the Pepsi' … 'Lip smacking, thirst quenching, ace tasting, motivating, good buzzing, cool talking, high walking, fast living, ever giving, cool fizzing Pepsi!' These were the lyrics to the new television Pepsi advert.

These were some of the 70s sayings that I had to get my head around if I was to survive my first week; can you dig it, dream on, far out, and right on? Yes exactly!

The educational system was a tad frosty with me, and that's putting it mildly. School was stifling and oppressive and seemed unending. I wasn't interested in history, maths, inflation or politics. I was however interested in having fun, fun, fun. Sports day was always greeted with open arms because it was competitive with proper races and personal rosettes. The other things I really enjoyed at Bodmin Comprehensive were art, music, drama, the band I drummed in called (Vanilla Moth) and admiring the girls. The band was made up of four of us: Alex Hudson, the late Michael Mullis (Mole), Paul Shreer and myself. We had all purchased our own second hand instruments. Lead, rhythm and bass guitars, and a drum kit with two cymbals. Months later we bought second hand amplifiers. The mixture of music, our band, drama, fun and the girls were perfect for me. Our newly arrived music teacher Mike Pettican had played in the Dave Clark Five band in their early days. This was the man who supported us setting up our school rock band. He would spend hours trying to show us some guitar licks. However, not quite what I was looking for considering I was on the drums. I can't really be sure why was he so keen to get all four of us in a band? Maybe he thought we had real potential.

Could he accommodate our rock star longings by teaching us all how to play properly? He was a good music teacher, but he could never open the music room on time because he was always leaving his keys on the piano. For me he was a forward thinking teacher who we could all relate to and respect. Our band covered a lot of Slade songs. If you can remember most of their record titles on the Polydor label were spelt wrong: 'Cum on feel the noize', 'Take me bak ome', 'Look wot you dun' and 'Coz I luv you'. This really confused me, so I wrote a short letter to the lead singer Noddy Holder to say how disappointed I was in the fact that the band were really screwing me up with their spelling, and how I was getting further behind in my English exams (this bit isn't true). During the 70s, Slade became one of Europe's biggest bands. You couldn't miss Noddy Holder's full on vocal. They would tour and record continuously, producing a catalogue of hits that became synonymous with the era and providing a soundtrack for the new glam generation. Even to this day, Slade are still one of the loudest, exciting, raw live bands on the road, their stage performance is a dynamic, powerful and invigorating roller coaster ride of pure rock.

Being in a band, doing art and drama, I thought all of this was the be-all and end all. I have always been a visual person, which meant photos, paintings, album covers, logos and pictures from magazines, anything that would inspire me. When it came to drawing in art class I was constantly reprimanded for attempting to draw T.Rex performing on stage, or Bowie singing Ziggy Stardust rather than delivering an average piece of work. My teacher would say, 'Paul, we don't make art for the public, we are the public that make art, now bin this and start again.' I had to sit with my teacher every eight weeks to discuss my chosen CSE subjects, four of which were PE, Art, Home Economics and Drama. I felt I was being grilled for an hour, you know when the light is shone in your face. At that precise moment I sat there thinking, 'What if I fail PE? Isn't that a bit like failing lunch!'

I felt quite energised at the thought of being creative within these subjects. In fact, six of us went on to make a twenty-minute film in drama entitled 'Why?' My enthusiasm wasn't to last though. When I chose these subjects for my lessons my teacher said he knew why I had chosen them, it was because they were straightforward to get through and a cop out. Bit harsh I thought to myself. Surely there was a glimmer of hope somewhere.

It never seemed to matter what I had to say in the classroom, whether it was positive or negative. I would just end up sitting back in my chair, hands behind my head waiting for the self-righteous, frothy, poisonous hatred to come towards me. Usually completely overlooking the point I had made about something worthwhile. Then came the gushing venomous, fouled mouthed rage which would strike me like a lobotomised puff adder with Tourette's. Believe me, there was nothing 'Peace and Love' about this! They had three mottos: behave, don't forget to always behave, and remember not to forget the principles of how to behave. I couldn't or wouldn't. Every little episode lead me into the sin bin. Or should I say, I would be ready to be shot from the cannon.

Disillusioned but not beaten by the negative responses from my teachers, I battled on. I wasn't held back from self-doubt or self-criticism. Making a decision about what to commit my time and energy to came down to how I felt about something as opposed to what I thought about it. I despised the written work and study and found that this got in the way of my social time. I would clock watch, counting the seconds to the end of the wretched day. Bored to utter tears and chomping and chewing away on my bag full of Spangles, Refreshers and Tooty Frooties (my sherbet dib dabs had probably been confiscated the week before) I would pretend to be interested and engage by saying, 'Whatever.' I came home from school after my first day, my parents asked me, 'What did you learn today Paul?' I replied, 'Clearly not enough, I have to go back tomorrow.'

It wasn't helped by the fact that I had failed a few years at my Canadian school and was moved back a grade; this was a common theme throughout my school years. I would sit through most lessons gazing out the window, not listening, and had *no* intention of doing any of my work. I certainly knew how to tune out of any topics that didn't interest me. I guess at some point in my education I must have sat some exams however, I do not remember any of them, where they took place, nor what kind of questions I was asked to answer.

My school work was going from bad to worse, but in between all of this I was giving myself a wonderful lesson in confidence building. Confidence is a bit like a bucket with a hole in that we have to keep topping up. If you are seen as a confident person you will definitely have the upper hand. When your confidence is knocked, you seem to pay more attention to the reaction caused by something rather than to your own view of it. You become a slave to other people's opinions. I had a lot of friends and felt that my confidence and sense of humour always carried me throughout my school years. When the careers advisor came to visit the school and asked me what I wanted to do for a career I replied, 'Well I wouldn't mind being a rock star.' 'Oh,' they would say, 'Anyone in particular?' I loved the teacher training days as this meant time off. I had no ambitions and no idea what I wanted, let alone a career. My mind was anywhere but on education, maths eluded me.

My favourite, most listened to tracks at the time were, 'Stairway to Heaven' by Led Zeppelin, 'Imagine' by John Lennon, and 'Won't Get Fooled Again' by The Who. This was the music of my time, the music that made an impact on an impressionable young lad. These were the songs that I played over and over on my record deck whilst leaping around the front room. Nowadays when some of these songs come on the radio or I watch an old video or DVD clip, it really takes me back. A time when love was free, peace was the sign of the times and I felt we echoed the 60s. I guess I was on a trip of self-discovery and individual identity.

Chapter Three

My Part Time Jobs

As an energetic 16 year old teenager I held down three jobs, stacking them up one by one. First, I signed up to do a newspaper round for Bunt's newsagents at the top of Finn VC estate working six mornings a week. When bands brought out their new albums, I would get all the promotional stuff left over from the daily papers and weekly magazines. I would get badges, posters and stickers of Slade, Wizard, Bowie, Mud, The Sweet, T.Rex, Donny Osmond and David Cassidy. Interestingly enough, the girls either liked Donny Osmond or David Cassidy, but not both at the same time.

I was aware back then that David Cassidy was adored by the public. I was also aware that he was responsible for raking in the money for his record company, and the group owners of these weekly magazines and papers. With his striking looks and singing ability, combined with well written songs, Cassidy was a teen idol in waiting. Hits with 'Could It Be Forever', 'How Can I Be Sure' and 'Daydreamer'. It appeared that nothing could go wrong in his career. I remember one magazine called '45' which had all the words to the latest top twenty in it. I used to make sure I grabbed this one because it was sometimes hard to hear the lyrics the first time round on *Top of the Pops*. I had read all sorts of articles about the jobs pop stars had had to take before they became famous. Working in fish and chip shops, gravediggers and selling goods in markets. Somehow it made them authentic.

At the weekends in the evenings, I became a waiter at our local Chinese Restaurant. Then I met Paul Parnell who delivered milk on the estate where I lived and was delivering papers. Paul's parents owned the very first local taxi service, 'Parnell's Taxi Service' in Bodmin, starting off with one taxi. As years went by they expanded and ended up becoming a big company. I had now been delivering papers for five weeks. Paul had always said hello when we crossed each other on the paths. One morning he approached me and had a short conversation about working for him on a weekend basis, there was no interview. Without any hesitation I jumped into his milk float and off we went to work. I became one of the local Bodmin milk boys working for another local firm, Cornish Dairy. I'd never smelled so much incense on one estate in my entire life. Rod Stewart's 'Maggie May' was playing on the radio. The blonde spiky haired singer with the gravelly voice was now heading en route for a solo career, and almost half a century of rock and roll under his belt; the man who would become Sir Rod.

As we approached our first house we would pass the Corona man in his van, delivering bottles of dandelion and burdock, cream soda and cherryade. Paul gave me a run down on the dos and don'ts of my employment contract: (1) I don't expect you to sleep in, but if you do, don't blag your way out of the fact that you have; (2) Please be conscious about waking people up so early in the morning; (3) There are no doors to slam on the float; we do not have a diesel engine to wake anyone; (4) Be careful you don't skid on dog's poop; (5) You need to build up confidence on the round, and then you will develop the milk boy swagger (this meant that I would walk-bounce purposefully, with confidence); (6) Be polite and courteous at all times; never let me catch you being rude; (7) Under no circumstances will there be any hanky-panky with our customers (I turned a bit red at this point, but pointed out to Paul that this was just wind); (8) Do not deliver milk to anyone's house if you see dog's growling. If the owner says, don't worry they won't bite, run! (9) Continue ringing the doorbell, if you see the curtains moving slightly, and they haven't opened the door then this means that they haven't paid for three weeks; and (10) Remember who has informed you that they have gone on holiday. There is nothing worse than returning to 144 putrid milk bottles on your doorstep. Sound advice.

What I was really looking forward to was riding in the milk float, going down a hill doing 25 mph. Our float went a bit faster than the others. As the convoy of floats set off down Hillside Park's steep hill we gradually overtook most of them. The prize would be a pot of clotted cream to take home to your parents. Paul informed me that he had started his milk round three years before I joined him; he said he never looked back (except when reversing of course). Working in the Hillside Park estate, I got to know people really well. They would invite me to their house warming and birthday parties. I even had the privilege of attending a wedding. I gave them deluxe coloured plastic milk bottle covers for a wedding present!

Milk was only delivered in bottles back then; customers would leave handwritten notes if there were any changes to their orders. We also delivered so much more, and became pretty much a corner shop on four wheels. This included eggs, orange juice, bread, cigarettes and anchor butter. This butter was something else. Can anyone remember the advert? 'If you want a better butter, there's no other name you'll utter, because Britain's better butter tastes nice.' This was all very well, but the truth was we all bought Echo margarine because it was so much cheaper!

The hours were unusual; our first delivery was at 04.30. Once finished we would drive back to the depot where we would unload the empties, clean the float, and get ready for another day. At 14.30, when everything was spotless, I would head home to wash off the whiff of milk and cream. Our cat was always waiting for me at the doorstep; her name was Sterilised. I would then have a quick snooze at 3pm for an hour then straight out to socialise. Some Saturday nights we would head off to the Bodmin cinema to watch films like *Grease*, *Jaws*, and *Dirty Harry*. Some of the most well-known movie stars of the 70s were Paul Newman, Robert Redford and Burt Reynolds. Going to the cinema was a rare treat back then. The multiscreen cinemas of today weren't around for us then. Today, people would complain at the lack of choice and viewing and would find this inconvenient. It felt special going to the cinema. You had to queue up to buy your ticket as there was no bookings in advance. If you were late, there was no guarantee of making it to the front before the film had sold out.

Fridays would always take an age to arrive. It was crucial that I kept on the right side of my parents throughout the week if I wanted to attend a disco over the weekend. I also learnt that keeping some floor space free in my bedroom helped! One of the major decisions to be taken was which tracks I would play while I was getting ready to go out. These tracks had to get you in the mood for what was to come that evening. My favourite thing about this round was probably that Paul and I got to see a lot of things early in the morning that got missed by Joe public; we were often the first on the scene after incidents that had happened in the night. We would become another set of eyes and ears for the community. Quite often we would see foxes strolling around.

What a great idea this was because in a way I was getting a double wage for doing both jobs at the same time, a win -win situation. You have to take into account the level of independence and responsibility this milk–paper round brought into my life, I would benefit from it. I remember the buzz of shouting out loud for a bit of fun, 'Extra, extra, read all about it!' in the middle of the estate. I was very careful on my first paper–milk round closing all the gates behind me; I tried not to leap over any fences. John Noakes from my favourite legendary *Blue Peter* had taught me not to do this. (Mind you, *Grange Hill* was also a great show and a useful manual for surviving school.) You would soon learn to cross from one side of the road to the other between odd numbers and even numbers, although at times they would all run into one.

I always had a smile for the customers; I would pretend that I liked their pets, especially their Rottweilers! (The ones with metal coat hangers rammed down their pink frothy chops!) You would always hear the sound of a dog yapping or growling approaching a house. Sometimes you were nearly knocked off your feet if it was let loose, which is when you froze. Many a time I felt my heart hammering against my ribs as if it was trying to fight its way out of my chest. I was aware that I had to build good relations with all of the customers. Believe me if anyone ever complained, a mega drama would unfold. I had to wait four weeks before I received any feedback as to how I was doing. It eventually came and the feedback was that I was doing fine with no complaints from any of my customers.

Every Friday after school I would meet up with Paul, and off we would go to collect the weekly milk money. The UK had just switched to decimal currency. We would carry cards in our pockets which would explain and convert the new currency which was called New Pence. A lot of our customers just didn't understand this new money, our elderly customers thought this currency change was an excuse to increase milk prices. One customer grumbled, 'Just when you think your making ends meet, someone moves the ends!' I always found this to be a bit of a headache because part of my role was to tally up the weekly milk bill and request the money. Paul was a stickler for keeping the finance books transparent and that was fine. I would knock on the door, whilst waiting for a reply I would be adding up the figures with my fingers. Customers wouldn't see me doing this as I would turn to one side whilst they had their heads buried inside their hand bags looking for notes and coins. If I had to include counting with my toes, I would end up falling through their porch doors! This went down a treat this did.

One lady would always give me tea, biscuits and toast at least two weekends out of four. 'Cup of tea, love?' She would always be fine with me when dunking my chocolate digestive biscuits in my tea, and using my fingers fishing around for the soggy bits that had fallen into my cup. I could get away with this because like Paul, we liked a good old laugh and chat with the customers. You can never know people properly until you have had a cuppa with them in their own home. Tea is always the answer, or introduction to most things. Brooke Bond, Lipton's or Typhoo would do. However, on this occasion we were way behind. 'Where have you been?'

Paul would ask with a narked tone in his voice, 'Oh, I was just assisting one of our customers to get her washing machine working, a sock was lodged in the spinner,' I would reply. As we drove off I happened to look in the wing mirror and noticed strawberry jam and toast crumbs smeared all over my chops! It always seemed to be the middle aged women that wanted help to move furniture, or wanted something fixed. Where were all their husbands? Surely they weren't all working away!

I was taken back one morning when I was asked to deliver a message to another customer, 'Can you tell so and so at number xx not to come here until after 10.30.' ('Interesting', I would say to myself.) I would always try to avoid the next house. This was the lady who used to give me a pleasant smile, then yank my cheek and say that she wished she was twenty years younger. I'll be on my way then, gosh she had a lotta bottle.

Was it the shirts I wore that customers liked? I say this because one morning awaking at 04.30 to meet Paul I was only just on time. I was never usually late, but this morning I was. I had woken up five minutes before meeting up for work and grabbed some clothes on the landing, got dressed and ran out the house. I wasn't one to swipe the alarm clock off the shelf and pull the duvet over my head. What, stay in bed and not be bothered? Come rain, snow, or sleet I would always step up to the plate and deliver. I was never fatigued. Setting a fierce pace, always quick, and always thinking on my feet. Milk rounds weren't for faint hearted teenagers. I would be annoyed if I was late as I would miss my breakfast. I was always fussy about my cereal and I was never overly keen on Puffa Puffa Rice, it always had to be Frosties. On this occasion the packet was all but empty; that meant that when I got home I could cut out and make the complicated tiger model on the back of the packet.

I ran out of the house and caught up with Paul on the estate. It was still very dark up until 8am when we delivered milk and collected the money at the same time. Whilst standing at the doorway of one of our long standing customers I rang the bell and she opened the door. (This one always liked a chat and a laugh.) She stood there looking very confused, there was very little conversation and she wasn't her normal self. As I walked away which seemed like seconds, I put it down to her having a bad start to the morning and said just this to Paul when I got back into the milk van. 'No Paul,' he said, 'It's because you are wearing a woman's blouse!' What? No way! Whoops, wrong top. I had grabbed my sisters blouse instead of my shirt! It could have been a lot worst though, imagine puffed up shoulders! This never happened again, all my clothes were checked the night before under a bright lamp, five times. It's no good crying over spilt milk!

On one occasion, I was in conversation with a dear customer who was an elderly lady who lived on her own. She was really getting stuck into this debate about the youth of today. I was trying to get my side of the story across when the next minute she walked off saying, 'Right I haven't got all day to talk to you, I have to go now as my neighbour is here and she needs to help me onto the commode!' I only had one grumpy customer on my rounds, he would whinge about everything. I had noticed on several occasions that he wore sun glasses when he came to meet me at the door, even when it was raining. I asked him why he wore these and he replied, 'Because your whizzing personality blinds me!'

Then there was the man across the road who I could never get away from. 'Here Paul, the best way to produce great-tasting milk is to look after the cows. If the cows are well kept and healthy, and eat good quality food, they will return the favour with good quality milk.' This was a part time job, I wasn't overly bothered in undertaking an educational module on cows. Smiling nicely I would head off up the garden path. I could still hear him shouting out to me from the next garden. 'Did you know that cows have four stomachs and chew their food twice, regurgitating it and chewing the cud to help with digestion.'

You really did see how the other half lived dashing up to people's doorways with bottles and papers in your hand. People would be watching you at their windows and as soon as you deposited the paper through the letter box, the door would open straight away. One lady would always wait for us and as soon as we drove up her drive she would sing the Herman's Hermits hit, 'No milk today my love has gone away, the bottle stands forlorn, a symbol of the dawn.' For some people, we were the only visitors they would have all week, so it was important to spend a bit of time with them. They could hear our float humming along in the mornings, and the rattle of the milk bottles in their crates. You would see people washing and placing the bottles back on the porch for us to take back and re-use.

Quite often you would come back to a house hours later to collect the milk money and find that the silver foil milk bottle tops had been pecked in by the birds. Or, the milk would freeze in the winter and shoot ice cream out of the bottle top. Some customers would leave out a slate to put on top, that stopped them. The slugs were a right pain. I hated the feel of them if they were crawling down the bottles, repulsive! If people had a lot of plants, and it had been drizzly, half of the written messages about changes to orders, or the cheques left out ended up in a ball of papier mâché. It was a nightmare if the slugs had chomped away at the signatures of the cheques. On another note, you always knew when things weren't right when four full milk bottles were still outside the front door from the previous day or so. This usually meant that people were unwell.

House doors weren't locked and you would go into the kitchen to collect the money left on the table. There would be money left for the butcher, fish man and the milkman all in separate envelopes. Meat and coffee were really expensive; most people could hardly afford it. You knew when someone was well off if they left an envelope for this order. We all worried about the price of everything. It became the decade of raging inflation. Prices just went up and up, year after year at a shocking rate. Every customer was talking about the cost of living. Sometimes you would look in the fridge and check to see how much milk there was. I soon learnt what milk and extras our customers around Bodmin wanted – a half pint here, three pints there. A half-pound of butter on a Friday, twelve eggs and a quarter of Cornish clotted cream on a Saturday.

I enjoyed Saturdays delivering the milk early in the morning; seeing the sun rise over the Bodmin Jail. I would hear families getting ready to start their day. I would elevate my rubber neck and look into their kitchen windows; my eyes would lock onto the laid breakfast table, never one to miss out on anything. I could see our customers eating fried bread, plum tomatoes, poached eggs, beans, sausage and crispy bacon, which would be tantalising. It would then be washed down with a cup of steaming hot tea. One day I fell off the steps and ended up with a black eye; that will teach me to be nosey. I might have finished my rounds earlier if I had bounced from house to house sitting on my space hopper. Mind you, knowing my luck I might have bounced through someone's window and landed in their front room, 'Morning!'

Paul and I were totally baffled one December Saturday morning whilst delivering the Christmas pints. The bottle tops were designed with holly and Christmas puddings. This was the usual design for the jolly season! Milk sales were up on Christmas Eve due to the milk and biscuits left out for the reindeer. Of course, you would see all the Christmas festivities in each and every house, and if I had accepted all the alcoholic drinks I was offered I would never have got the milk delivered. One or two of the cantankerous old milkman that I knew would suddenly cheer up at Christmas time and try to be their customer's best friend. Anything to do with tips?

Customers came to their doors and started calling Paul and myself 'Ernie!' We didn't get it at all and looked at each other, 'Ernie?' we said. Then the next customer gave us two t-shirts with 'Ernie' written on the front. What was going on? Later that week watching *Top of the Pops* it all clicked, Benny Hill was in the charts with *Ernie*, who 'drove the fastest milk cart in the west'. Great! You wouldn't have minded if the name was Clint, Brad, or Elvis, but … Ernie! The song reached number one on 11 December 1971 and remained at the top of the charts for four weeks, including Christmas week. It was finally superseded by the New Seekers *I'd Like To Teach The World To Sing*. Benny's lyrics were fictional, but were loosely based on his memories of working as a milkman for Hann's Dairies.

My papers got all smudged in the snow and rain, staining my hands which were far from hygienic to the eye. I soon learnt not to wipe my face if I didn't want to end up wearing a black moustache. Some days you thought your shoulder was going to snap in half with the strain of carrying your double Cornish Guardian bags, the weight was enough to stunt your growth. In the winter my poor fingers would be numb from folding seventy odd papers – that fierce nip in the air. My freezing fingers would plunge into my warm pockets, it would be bitterly cold, especially when it was snowing – the big angry flakes that went for your eyes. I would sit in the heater-less float shivering under three coats, thick socks, boots, hat and a pair of gloves. I slogged on knowing that the afternoon would soon come around.

I never spoke to the other paper boys that worked on the other estates, but we would nod at each other. One day when I was close up, I observed that one of them had a lazy eye and wore a pink plaster over one of his lenses of his wire rimmed John Lennon NHS glasses. It always amazed me how he managed to stroll up the garden paths in a single line and get his papers through the letter box straight! Work that one out. Months later I would be carrying four papers under each arm, six bottles of milk with the bottle necks clutched between each of my fingers. Ernie could go and swing.

The weekends were long. Saturdays you had to double up on every order. However, at the end of the weekend you were assured of two things. First, your brown envelope full of dosh, and secondly a breakfast at Paul's parents' house. They lived next door to the Bodmin Jail. Twelve weeks in I could tell I was going to have an exceptional customer relationship. My mind was already gliding towards tip assessments. Good tippers would always be the ones who would say 'Keep the change', because you had gone the extra mile, those additional duties. I would accept these tips with agreeable eyes, closing the doors and gates behind me. I did my hardest not to flaunt my wealth when back at school. I was at the pinnacle of my game – I had mastered the milk–paper round. It was evident that Paul had never before seen flawlessness in a milk boy. I gave him no hard times, only once was I late, and I delivered. One day I overheard him talking to the other drivers who also had milk boys. 'Best milk–paper boy ever' I heard him say. The other drivers just scowled at me mimicking 'Best boy ever eh?'

Over time, I enjoyed a lot of good natured banter with a vinyl collector and his family about our respective favourite bands. It was a guaranteed way to get chatting. The more you put into the job, the more you got out of it. I would always try and help out a bit. We would also be asked to look out for customers lost dogs or cats; I spotted a dog of the description that was given to me and held on to it until the owner came. I was given a bag full of spangles from the dog's owner. Whenever I found keys in a front door, I would always push them through the letter box. It was a good job that I wasn't into borrowing cars for joy rides! Or was I?

The milk–paper round lasted a few years and I loved every minute of it. To this day I still miss it, and all the guaranteed daily humour we would have. Nothing like today eh? You wouldn't dream of leaving money out on your doorstep in either an envelope or under the mat, nor full milk bottles come to think of it. As for your brass knocker! Doorstep deliveries have been dying out for years now because customers have wandered off to supermarkets to do all of their shopping. Will people use milk delivery services again? I really do feel that it's going to take more than nostalgia to float people's milk floats! It's quite bizarre to think that I started this job with Paul in 1971, and this is now over 48 years ago – it seems just like yesterday. I would never have a bad word said against Paul, in fact I owe him massively. He will always be the one who gave me the milk round job, thus providing me with some of my fondest teenage memories. After all, being a milk boy was one of the most sought after jobs. This job also represented the perfect platform to showcase that deep down I did possibly have some useful skills.

Back in the 70s you became pretty self-sufficient. You could even sell lemonade and doughnuts without a permit. Well I did grow up in a time when you had to work hard to get what you wanted. I just didn't want to sit on my backside wasting time as there was so much energy there if I was going to do these jobs then let's crack on and do them properly. It also allowed me to purchase my own clothes, kept the vinyl arriving, and have the funds to see those live bands. Having three jobs I decided not to tell my parents that I was becoming very well off, including the odd pocket money that came my way. Not forgetting the tips which would take care of any new aftershaves for the weekend. You see having a smile as a young lad did bring in a bit extra. Yearly, I would receive more than fifty pounds in tips, and given presents at Christmas time. The pound note always seemed to go a long way back then. If you had a few of these you were considered well off. It seemed like life was pretty affordable, and wages seemed to cover my simple needs. The pounds I received for those hard-sweat hours were like gold. What I learnt on the way was that the harder I worked, the more I got. Hard work never bothered me. To be honest I love hard work as much as doing nothing at all.

Chapter Four

Dreaded School

The down side to all of this was that I could hardly keep my eyes open during the first Monday of each week when returning to school. I used to sit at the back of the class in order to get my head down on the desk and sleep. My teacher would say, 'Come on Paul wake up, you're not supposed to sleep so blatantly in the class whilst the rest of us are learning.' Peeling my face off the desk and dribbling saliva into my Beatle pencil case, I would apologise, scooping up my dignity (and my saliva). I've received a few clips around the ear for not paying attention, whether I deserved them or not is another question. Okay, I might have been reading the odd Beano comic in class, but that's beside the point. At the end of each weekend I just wanted to crawl into my bed and sleep.

I wasn't shy of work or people; this also demonstrated again that I thrived on interacting with people. Paul was a good boss to work for and like Alfie Symonds (more of whom later) played an enormous role in my teenage life. They listened to me and were fun, they really thought about what I had to say and would come back with an adult answer, which was outside of your parents' views and very healthy. After all I was only a young teenager, a juvenile pup.

What was the worse was the school system I was in. Secondary school was becoming a difficult jungle to navigate, it was getting in my way again. Teachers wanted dedication, keenness and organisation, someone who would shine. I would spend a great deal of time trying to intercept letters that the school had sent to my parents to inform them yet again about another episode. Rather than just telling me and others to be quiet, they would have their own way of keeping all of us in some sort of order; they would wrap us over the knuckles with a thick ruler. Nowadays they would be prosecuted for treating us in a manner like this. It's called 'child cruelty'. Back then it was called 'internal keep it discreet discipline'. Most of my teachers had sold their souls. The badge that I wore read, 'Four teacher signatures equalled detention' (on the cusp of earning another one).

Teachers were certainly a different breed back in the 70s. You seemed to get punished for just about everything. Even then some teachers realised that this was wrong, especially when a wooden cup full of pens was thrown across the classroom and hit me on the head. 'Ouch', I felt that one. Somehow, they could manage to throw objects from one end of the classroom to the other and still manage to hit you. You wouldn't have minded so much if it was screwed up balls of paper. The point I am making is that nobody should have to put up with it. On one occasion the teacher threw a board duster at me, so I picked it up and threw it back at him. The satisfaction of my retaliation was well worth the frustration of the battle with these demanding, high maintenance, railroading, dictating, short sighted, control-obsessed, cynical buffoons. The classroom was their stage, the green light for persistent oppression. Something wrong would continue to remain wrong. I often wondered how many kids ended up traumatised for long periods of their lives because of this. Talented teachers? Now safe to ignore!

I was completely bored. I'm a practical doer, not a sitter. One day I threw my pen down, swung round and wiped all my books straight off the desk in pure frustration, shouting out loud, 'I've had enough of this drivel.' No one batted an eyelid. Surely we should have been taught to think for ourselves and problem solve without being spoon fed. Our classes back then were certainly not places for any lively debate. I honestly think that my teachers lacked patience and understanding, so in the end you grew up feeling pretty dense in your early teens. I started to express myself on paper; reading it back it helped me to see things clearer. One of the main difficulties I found was trying to make sense of many of the subjects I was being taught.

The deliverance method seemed laboured and impersonal. I found an old report recently that read 'Paul has still not learnt to channel his energies in the right areas. Both his work and behaviour continue to remain erratic and he requires greater control over them. He is attention seeking, disruptive, disinterested and boisterous. Please deal with these issues.' I thought I did really well having played hard five days a week! I would always push the boundaries as far as I could, to see what would happen. I had nothing to lose here. On the big day of celebration in the classroom of doom and gloom, my classmates would stand alongside each other, hands folded together. Everyone would be given their school report in the classroom at least thirty minutes before the end of term, sealed in a large brown envelope that would remain that way until your parents opened it.

Reports were always an unbearable day for me, a time for commiserating. I would have loved to have been a fly on the wall when teachers discussed me, to witness the eyes rolling. I always wondered what the discussions were in their staff room, 'Who Deacon? What a nightmare, he needs to go.' I remember writing my own report on a piece of coloured paper, it read, 'I am delighted with what you have achieved this year Paul. Well done and keep up the good work!' This would be signed by wishful thinking. It's absurd that one would expect everyone to deliver the same way in school. I would be saved every time from answering that dreaded question, by the bell signalling the end of the lesson. Different people learn differently – we certainly know more about learning differences now than what we did in the 70s.

I signed up to a woodwork class and thought, 'this is okay.' I wasn't exactly sure what I was doing but whilst carving a piece of square wood on a lathe I decided that this would be a base for a table lamp and soldiered on carving the wood into a circle. My parents would be real proud with the finished product, I thought to myself. I was really chuffed and stood there with one hand on my hip, the other hand carving, staring around the class. It was very much look at me and how well I'm doing with this; bit cocky looking back. Something in my head was telling me that this was all going to go dreadfully wrong. It did! The next minute I heard 'Whoosh!' The wood had spun off the lathe. The whole class of thirty ducked and hid behind doors as pieces of wood went spinning through the air. I thought, 'where's that come from?' Then I realised it was me. 'Oh dear' I thought. My woodwork teacher went ballistic. Eek!

He fixed me with that hard-as-nails stare he had perfected over the years. I think he took my open-mouthed stare as his green light to go the whole hog. 'Come here boy,' he shouted. I walked slowly towards him like a collie dog who was about to be told off for stealing Sunday's chicken. 'What's your name,' he shouted? 'What?' I thought, 'you know my name'. 'It's Paul.' 'No it's not, it's Billy,' he said. 'Billy?' I thought. 'No it's Paul,' I replied. He shouted again, 'No it's not it's Billy, Silly Billy.' At times you would feel like you had been eaten up and spat out like a slippery kipper. My thinking at the time was the two most powerful things to give your teacher would be a clipboard and a shiny badge. What he gained from saying this in front of everyone is beyond me, clearly a teacher whose head was full of sawdust. He was certainly no guide for the pigs; and his moods were up and down like a toilet seat. They did themselves no favours with their brash, in your face, bullying tactics. Presumably they thought that by making an example of someone out in the open, that others would think twice before challenging them. Get real!

I was aware that I had been singled out for the worst of his tongue lashing abuse, but it just made me stronger. I would survive this. I also knew I was on a rocky road because only a week before he had asked me my name and I said, 'Paul.' He replied, 'You should say Sir first.' 'Ok', I said, 'Sir Paul.' The following week I attended his lesson. He walked into the class and swept his arm across the work bench to clear everything, ever so dramatic saying, 'Okay, are we going to do this or not.' I was thinking to myself, you're a jerk. I would walk away thinking, so if teachers think they are so smart why are they still at school? I had hardly ever allocated any time to sit down and read anything. I thought that was just so boring. I always felt that I had to be doing something more active. I also felt that there was some sort of mild dyslexia problem throughout my entire school life. This is something that just wouldn't have been picked up back in the 70s; it wasn't deemed a problem in those days, or put more precisely, it was only a problem if you were dyslexic yourself. Since no one had ever heard of this being unable to read, write or spell properly just really meant that all my teachers and the rest of my classmates thought I was either plain stupid, mega stupid, or down right lazy … great!

Although my spelling is still poor at times, I have managed to overcome the worst of my difficulties through training myself to focus and concentrate a lot more. Most people I have discussed this with over the years totally dismiss what I have to say, they don't see the effort I have to go through, but it really can be hard. Technology has certainly helped a hundred percent, especially my computer and iPad. Computers have revolutionised all of our lives and have that power to enlighten and educate us on a daily basis. Maybe my early problems with what I thought was dyslexia made me more intuitive; when faced with facts and figures to study, I find that my imagination grips and expands on the content of what I am reading. Knowledge back then certainly wasn't like it is today. If something appeared in print – whether in a book or a newspaper – it was taken as fact. Of course today is a very different story.

At one stage I was technophobic, but soon grasped the technique and ran with it. You had to because we now live in a society of communication through mobile phones, email, fax, Twitter, and Facebook. Welcome to the split second hi-tech internet driven world where anyone and anything can spring up on the internet within seconds. Bang, done! Whoops, it's now in black and white. 'Oh, well that can get you into trouble can't it? Hey ho such is life!' These devices could make life more dangerous and stressful if used inappropriately. If all of this had been around in my youth and I had done something foolish, it would have been plastered all over YouTube or Facebook the next day! I do think that people need to step away from social media and bond with real human beings. Close the laptops, shut down the phones, and give it a break. Having said that, Google would have been a reliable friend back then, 'Hey google, why don't you just sit next to me during my next exam?' Better still if my pen could have copied and pasted. During exams I would look up for inspiration, down for desperation, or left and right for information. When the hand-held calculator came on the scene, I would sit at the back of the maths class, under the table!

I am fully aware that I was never easy as a child and could not and would not sit still for more than five minutes. I was into everything and mischievous. Boredom was always hovering, especially car journeys. 'Are we there yet?' 'Nope we've just left.' It appeared that my life was going to be two speeds: full on and full on. Running on Ever Ready batteries on a daily basis. Things that would make people shout out aloud, 'No Paul, don't do that!' came quite naturally to me, like testing the toaster with a metal knife whilst it was switched on to see if it was working. Or riding my push bike at twenty miles an hour down a steep hill, sticking my foot in the spokes of my front wheel to see how quickly I could stop.

Somewhere on East 22nd Avenue, Vancouver, there are imprints of my face on the road. Were there injuries? Yes of course. Hospital appointments? Yes of course. Did it happen again? Yes of course. I was never fazed by attending the Accident and Emergency Department, over time I built up a good rapport with all the staff. It was a frequent event to share beakers of fizzy cola with all the nurses whilst my plasters were being applied. As soon as they pronounced me officially repaired, I was off like a shot. However, there were times where I was left unable to walk on one leg, or eat anything due to injuries. For some reason I always wanted to be older than what I was. Indulging in all the usual street games, I always chose to keep in with the big lads, choosing to like bands that delivered a message. I would never do things in half measures.

I despised discipline big time, and rebelled against whatever came my way, flirting with authority if you like. If I was told you can't, I did. I was a rebel but never a malicious one, never a bully or cruel, just totally bored, restless and disinterested in what academia had to offer. I would always be on the lookout for something new and exciting to fill my time, anything to alleviate any boredom. Anyway, I hated to be pigeonholed. I have no hesitation whatsoever in saying that if all the daily risks were removed from my childhood environment, I would have been doomed to a life of playing it forever safe. I do not look back on my childhood or teenage days thinking, could've, would've, should've, maybes, might have, what if? I just did it. I most certainly wasn't a teenager who looked through rose tinted glasses.

My punishment for doing wrong would be two days grounded to the house and garden, which hurt every time. I was forever being grounded, or so it felt at the time. Most of my latter schooldays, I slid out of the house under the parental radar. What my parents didn't realise at the time was that whilst occasionally they thought this was punishment for me, I was in fact living a life of luxury. Summoning my mates on a daily basis to go to the local corner shop to purchase sweets and the odd comic book, along with tins of coke, and then hoisting the goods up in a bucket tied up by rope, to my bedroom window. This was the only time I put on weight. Round one to me! Of course, months down the road they caught onto this when the rope I used snapped trying to pull a reclining armchair up through my bedroom window. This was decidedly thumbs down. If the rope hadn't snapped, it would have been given official approval by my mates.

I have often reflected on the fact that life is made up of different people doing different things. But what are their dreams and ambitions, their visions and goals in life? Essentially, there are two kinds of people. There are those who want to climb the highest mountain, and others who are more than happy to sit and hang out at the bottom of the mountain sharing their pancake with whipped cream. For me, I wanted to climb to the top, but knew deep down that this was not a vision that others recognised. Why? Well if anyone expected a level of physical or academic excellence, or at least effort, from me at this stage then they were going to be let down in a big way.

Dissatisfaction and pent up frustration harboured for many years. At times I would feel that life was too safe, mundane, and I would crave excitement. There were times though that I found myself screaming into the wind and directing my efforts in entirely the wrong direction. In only my sixth week at Bodmin Comprehensive School, I was ordered to the headmaster's office having broken yet another rule. Back then I thought rules where there to be broken. If the rulebook was not being ripped up, it was certainly being thrown around the school playing field. 'Good morning Deacon' said the headmaster, swivelling round in his chair. Leisurely raising his head from the pile of papers on his desk, he took one look at my face and simply said with a grin, 'So what have you brought for me today?' He was so matter of fact about the whole incident that I withdrew my hand on the second cane lash for devilment. I couldn't work out if his offhand truculence was a studied pose or down to genuine awkwardness and nervousness.

The cane for which they had complete authorisation to smack you, was regularly administered to the palms of my hands. I informed the headmaster that the cane in England was much thicker than the strap that they used in my Canadian schools. (And then waited to see if his eyes also turned black.) Teachers were failing working class teenagers. Most of them hell bent on caning us into obedience rather than stimulating our brains. They had to have been a qualified teacher for three years before they could deliver this barbaric mistreatment.

Those that were close to me at the time were wise enough to know that it's almost impossible to convince others to learn by your mistakes, rather than their own. Perhaps some of my teenage patterns were doomed to be played out again and again. When close friends would curve on the side of caution for fear of offending you, it's so easy to believe that any disapproval has evaporated. The truth of it all is that seeing the integrity in someone else quite often has little effect on their behaviour. To me and looking back now, this surely was all part of growing up and being a teenager. Today, I have no qualms about admitting any issues or even failures.

There's no point in going to school today I kept saying to myself one morning while I was getting ready to put my mud stained uniform on. The day before I had been involved in an altercation with one of the Grammar School lads, the ones who had passed their eleven plus. They all wore duffle coats and grammar-school scarves, parading around like nerds. It was only after I had departed from education that I became really good mates with them all. I always questioned the validity of these schools. Sucking in the best teachers and pupils, causing a huge barrier across education as a whole. Grades were normally made public, and pupils with the best results ridiculed others who perhaps hadn't done so well. Competitiveness was ingrained in this system.

At least five times a month, I would walk into the school's main entrance, register, then shoot out the back door in a flash. I took note of the emergency exits early on. It was much better if a supply teacher was on duty that day because they didn't know you. I didn't need teachers teaching me about experiences they knew nothing about, so I went off on our local bus exploring other towns around us, St Austell, Wadebridge, and Liskeard to name a few. This was far better than sitting in a hot stuffy classroom and being totally miserable. The headmaster would always take a harsh view of any pupil skiving off school, and there was always a risk of getting caught either by the school board members, or someone who knew my parents. It was exciting though. I would travel all over Cornwall, dinner money permitting of course, especially on roast dinner days which were more expensive. Did I get caught? Yes of course! Was I punished? Yes of course! Did I do it again? Yes of course!

Was I that cheeky throughout my education? In my English class I was asked what the longest sentence I could think of was. I replied, 'That's got to be life imprisonment.' 'Why are you talking during my lesson?' I was asked by my teacher. I replied. 'Why are you teaching during my conversation?' My favourite pastime was when a few of us would use a compass to dig out holes in our desks to play golf. We used pencils for golf clubs and bits of rubber for the golf balls. This was great fun.

Towards the last final year of my education I was expelled. (Only days before I had stopped taking my school bag with me, and my pencil case.) I was really shocked, stunned when the head delivered this to me. In fact, I was quite dazed and couldn't hear exactly what the full content of the conversation was, but grasped the word expelled. He knew that I wasn't capable of being involved in this conversation. His voice sounded like he was talking under water. If that's what you have to do I thought sitting there with my head in my hands? At first, I was placing both hands against my numb ears. A knot was tugging in my stomach as I nervously felt fidgety. In my defence I didn't think this was justified. For the first time ever, I don't think I offered one single word to the conversation, just needed to sit and listen. The silence in his office was deafening.

I was quite relieved that no one saw me entering into the office and that I didn't have to endure any further humiliation. However, people saw me leaving and noticed my angst-ridden face. 'You okay Paul?' 'No,' I replied. On my way out I sighed and forced a smile. I would have to take responsibility for my own actions. Hours later I would be irritable and subdued. Many a time I was confronted by a panel of serious faces that would decide and deliver my fate. Not once did I feel that they gave me permission to make any mistakes. Surely there should have been room for a degree of growth. Accept your landing? Nope! Wouldn't expelling me blemish their school's record? Obviously not. What I needed was intensive tailored encouragement to get my education on track, not expelling! Was it really acceptable to let me leave without any exam results?

The next few weeks blended seamlessly from shock into boredom. Facing the future when I felt I was so far behind everybody else was quite daunting. It started to dawn on me that growing up into a young man was more complicated than I had thought. I saw no one coming to my rescue within our group of so called social and school mates. This was my first real inclination of becoming wary of those who could lull you into a false sense of security. I don't always put a great deal of trust in those that think they are doing the correct thing for me, as in looking out for me. We all know that people can drop you from a great height when it suits them. I learnt that it is far better not to put people in the position where they can do this in the first place – get my drift? From then on, I made a constant decision to have an arm's length relationship with certain people.

At that time, school meant nothing to me. I didn't get it whatsoever, and in return school made it quite clear that it didn't get me. So that was that I guess, confirming loud and clear there and then that school was finally over for me. How ironic that Alice Cooper had released his hit single, 'School's out'. In saying that though, it wouldn't be right not to mention that there were times where the odd subject grasped my attention. In later years, I would wonder if it might have been better if I had gone the whole traditional route and attended a lot more.

During my school years I had always had a dilemma within me: on the one hand, the desire to conform and do well, but on the other I wanted to be rebellious, kicking against the rigidity of the school timetable. I didn't want to offend too much; I wanted to see other points of view. I was saddened by this sense of failure, but the decision was made and now it was over. Believe me though, I was hurt by this sudden ending. Things were a bit tough to say the least and the future was very uncertain. My next big challenge was how I was going to unravel this 'news bulletin' to my parents. Each morning I would leave the house at the usual school time, spending time with friends and hanging out in Barbery's, my local café. Anything so that they wouldn't uncover what had happened. However, in the end I gave in and grassed on myself. I sat on the edge of the settee, with a white-knuckle grip on the cushion; it all came gushing out. Let's put it this way, after an hour my cat emerged from behind the settee, ears curled back. Coronation Street was on in the background.

With things getting even more fractious and beginning to spiral downwards, my teenage years became an absolute nightmare and I found myself proceeding down the juvenile route. It wasn't mega serious and nothing like today. I had myself written down as one of those bad boys; nothing too extreme, just living on that edge of delinquency. Okay I say delinquent but do I mean just being one of the lads. After all I did have a certain amount of awareness; my instinct to anything too off the mark would always steer me away. Isn't it about the spur of the moment and egging each other on? I only borrowed a few cars, had minor pub scrapes, and Pascoe's fish and chip shop-queue misunderstandings. I would lay awake at night worrying about the whole mess I was in. I would throw myself into doing anything, which would become my entire focus. It really was a problematic time with so much going on. I would use all those distractions to take my mind off what was happening.

The truth was it was a foggy mixture of lots of uncertainty; my head just seemed to be somewhere else. I did my very best to ignore those nagging feelings that I was walking through far too many wrong doors. Basically, it felt as if I was walking the plank. Eventually something happened that I decided was the final straw. Enough was enough. No one would have picked up on my inner turmoil, 'Dear stress, please can we end this relationship now, I don't want to be with you any longer.' I was in denial about many things, so I did the first thing I could think of. I postponed reality, because a dark storm cloud seemed to hover ominously over everything I did. Have you ever read this: 'Life isn't about waiting for the storm to pass, It's about learning to dance in the rain'? Well, years later I learnt how to dance in the rain.

These early years had been excruciating, but not enough to make me lie down or to make me much wiser at that time come to think of it. Though a bit bruised I still stood upright, brushed myself down, and clung on to some dignity. I still had enough fuel in my tank to see this through. I had let my life spin out of control, but at the end of the day we are all held responsible. Yes, we all have choices in life, perhaps not about what events life deals us, but rather what we choose to do about it. When I read about other people in the same situation it gave me a sense of not quite being so alone but in fact somehow connected to the wider world. We may choose not to answer our critics, but we must at least answer to ourselves. I went through the bit about life being unfair, and what makes sense is that it can be. If you accept this, then things are so much easier. So many people go through life unscathed whilst others receive more than their fair share.

I also struggled with the fact that I had let my parents down when they were such good parents to us all; it couldn't have been easy for them. I now see this time like a white-knuckle rollercoaster at the fair. I didn't for one moment think of looking behind me, to see that my parents were riding with me. I doubt very much that I made their lives a picnic. Also, I didn't realise at the time that memories would fade, the rawness of these events would start to blur a little over time. On reflection, some of us were just a group of wild lads eager to get out and about and have fun. I guess you could say that some of us liked to burn the candle at both ends. I was starting to feel that I just existed in this adult world. Deep down and quite understandably, I was uncertain about a lot of things. I didn't feel passionate about very much or bound to it in anyway, whatever the topic. The bottom line was I wanted to demonstrate I could handle what was happening in my life so that I would be included in everything.

Chapter Five

Fasten Your Seat Belts: Closure on My School Years

I have never bought into the cliché that your school days are the best days of your life. If the truth be known I truly despised authority back then, represented by the teachers who were interfering, judgemental and patronising. Disrespect breeds disrespect, and what I recall is a cluster of mindless drones from whom I learned nothing. To me they were obnoxious and condescending, total control freaks.

More often than not their subject delivery would be a dribbled, dreary monotone, boring and incomprehensible. They would go off on tangents and chew the fat or indulge in histrionics. Talking about one thing and then moving swiftly onto another without drawing breath. They had forgotten the basic life rules about treating people with respect and dignity, resorting to throwing chalk, board dusters, cups or anything else they could find across the classroom. Pathetic, ridiculous over reaction, high maintenance and totally orchestrated.

The 'happiest days of my life' left me with feelings of anger and resentment that are deeply ingrained. The teachers who should have set me up for life let me down in a big way.

But I rebelled, and I have channelled so much effort in my own life into becoming just the opposite to people like this. Some people were always so quick to put me down, but the fact is that sometimes I simply made bad choices or was a slow learner. Don't judge a book by its cover, especially mine!

It's good to hear that these days kids don't have to go through what we did.

Back then I had a tendency to dive into things without really thinking about the consequences. My early life was really a bit of a free for all, but I was always rescued by a good sense of humour.

Anyhow, I digress.

Okay, where was I?

Chapter Six

The Seventies

With no qualifications or hope it was a very limbo time indeed. The whole world was out there and I can remember walking home thinking 'now what?' No qualifications, and no work, I felt as if I'd been side-lined. This stuck in my throat like chicken bones. There was no time to be spent sitting on a pity pot. I had to stop, take stock and think about my next move. I would find refuge and go to my bedroom, put on my headphones and shut the world out. Carefully placing the LP onto my turntable, I would listen for those new sounds with eager ears, before drifting off to sleep. It was nothing to put a record on at 11pm and wake up at 2am hearing the sound of it clicking around the turntable.

My favourite musician, John Lennon, wrote a song called 'Working Class Hero'. The lyrics have always stayed with me: 'When they've tortured and scarred you for twenty odd years, then they expect you to pick a career, when you can't really function you're so full of fear'. These lyrics summed up my time during my school years. When you listen to the entire album 'Plastic Ono Band' in cold isolation, it's quite thought provoking. There were voices that kept me on the straight and narrow; Lennon was one of them. His voice was always distinguished through any Beatle track. Lennon would feed his pain and realism of his life into his new songs. The Beatles were and still are the best band in the world ever. Lennon and McCartney – the most successful writing team of all time – were the engine room of the band. Not one of the bands that I mention have ever stepped up to the plate like the four of them did. If Oasis had stopped trying to be the Beatles then they would be even more popular and would have sounded better than what they did. Basically, they were a reworking of what the Beatles had actually recorded. Do I like Oasis? Yes!

At the time I was young enough to believe that anything was possible, but also old enough to know that whilst possibilities may be endless, time was not. I really worried about wasting time, but I don't think time is ever wasted if you manage to make something creative out of it in the end. Here I was still living at home, but also having a good time. In most situations I would find something to laugh about; however bizarre I would turn it into a joke.

During the 70s, Britain had four prime ministers, four general elections, five official states of emergency, two property booms, two oil crises, a riot of youth subcultures and a pop music revolution whose cultural reverberations are still being felt. Fragmented, ambiguous decades such as the 70s have an advantage in the nostalgia market. They had a bit of something for everyone. Everything was different and this clicked with me. How you looked, dressed and did your hair was the key to way people identified you. Everyone appeared relaxed with what was going on around them. We were left pretty much to our own devices. I have a kaleidoscope of memories of these days. It felt like the entire generation was growing up from being just good boys and girls, into not-afraid-to-be-bad-if-needed, men and women.

I cannot help quoting the famous lines of Charles Dickens which realistically describe the experience of living through this era: 'It was the best of times, it was the worst of times. It was the age of wisdom, it was the age of foolishness. It was the epoch of belief, it was the epoch of incredulity. It was the season of the light, it was the season of darkness. It was the spring of hope, it was the winter of despair. We had everything before us, we had nothing before us.'

It was reassuring to know that good bands were around to take your mind off the lows. Ah the 70s, what a fantastic time that was. People had a very small slice of the pie instead of just the crumbs; there was less of a gap between the rich and the poor. There was also less traffic and pollution; society wasn't saturated with the media. Development wasn't swallowing up our wonderful wildlife and countryside, and all of the Beatles were still alive. I have to say that I think I would have liked to have brought my kids up in this era because we all spent so much time outside without the dreaded thought of anyone whipping you away. I also think that we were a lot more sociable and free back then to do whatever we wanted without someone breathing down our necks, 'Now listen here young laddie, that is not politically correct'. There are far too many restrictions these days, it's ludicrous.

I would literally be out all day, and if I did pop home I would simply walk through the back door, grab a packet of crisps, and walk out the front door. Sometimes without saying anything. My friends and I would ride our bikes, kick around a ball, roll around in fields, sprint through the sprinkler. Time was spent finding insects and putting them in jars. Buying popsicles with two sticks that you could break in half and share with your mates. Laughing so hard that your stomach ached. Being tired from running around. Giving your friends a ride on the handle bars of your bike. Going on trips with a picnic of soggy egg sandwiches. Throwing water balloons. Being taken to the cafeteria by your parents for a treat. Family parks were always open and had awesome equipment to play on. There was a free spirit in the air. I would return home most nights when the street lights started to come on.

I think it is an experience absent from the lives of so many kids today. I can't help questioning if the restriction of kids' freedom exacerbates the increase in behavioural disorders such as attention deficit hyperactivity disorder (ADHD). After all, how many of our kids get to run around for hours on end, working off their excess energy? It really makes you think because, in the long gone days of my childhood, it was the norm for us all to be physically and socially active outside. 'Go on out you go, a bit of rain won't hurt you!' I would hear as I passed through the neighbourhood where kids were being flung out of their houses. It appears that nowadays this is an exception rather than the norm. So many kids have no understanding of the freedom that shaped their parents' youth. When I look back at some of my old photographs of me and my mates, I think goodness gracious what a bunch of lean kids we were. But lean was the standard. Yes, you would have the odd plump one in there amongst us, but they would be the only one out of a class of thirty-odd. Even the plump one wasn't huge.

Other things that come to mind was the fact that people ate food from tinned cans. Baby cots were painted with dazzling lead paints. There were no childproof caps on any of the medicine bottles. We rode our second hand customised bikes with no helmets. We would hitchhike and get lifts from town to town. Sitting on Dad's lap and operating the steering wheel. Car seats? My dad drove me around on the back shelf of his Ford Galaxy. 'Oops, Paul was there a minute ago, must have hit a bump.' Jumping on beds until they collapsed. I was once under my bed when that happened, what a mess! Babysitting at 14. Once you were capable of dialling 999 you were considered a candidate for babysitting jobs. Being totally far away from after school or camp until our evening meal. Now, we would call that being lost.

Playing on a rusted swing set where that one leg always popped out of the ground threatening to thrust you into space and then came back with a thud. We drank water from dirty hose pipes, shared bottles of fizz with someone else's crumbs floating on the top. We ate white bread and sugary cakes. We nicked fruit and vegetables from the local allotments. We fell off walls, got tangled in barbed wire, ripped our clothes, tumbled out of trees, broke bones and cracked teeth. We didn't think anything of it, and if we did it would be, 'Get over it.' I didn't see anyone calling the police because we were playing out in the street, or in the park without our parents. I don't remember going out with a rucksack overflowing with knee and elbow pads, plasters, and paracetamol. Our parents gave us more freedom in our decision making. They didn't really feel the need to provide for our every whim to please us. We were left to make our own mistakes no matter how painful it was to them. It was left to us to accept responsibility for our actions, and deal with the after effects.

Some of my friends' parents would blow a whistle at 9pm every evening. This was to give the signal that it was time to come in. It was nothing to hear distinctive whistle sounds around our neighbourhood. Our school sandwiches were leftover luncheon meat; we didn't have fridges in classrooms or ice blocks in our lunch boxes. We did not get food poisoning. There were no safety nets on trampolines. They would be hosed with water, and a squirt of washing up liquid to make it even more slippery. What was said in the playground stayed in the playground. We were enrolled with the school nearest to us, not the best school some forty miles away. Tree houses were built by us as kids, not bought from toy shops. Pass the parcel had one winner. Meat was purchased from the local butcher and packed without a use-by date. My mum used her nose to tell if the lamb chops were off.

When you got caught by the local policeman doing reckless things, you received a set of sizzling ears. You were then frog marched home to your parents, where you got the other half. I was also very aware that the 70s were not a decade to be timid in. All this may sound like an under-privileged childhood, but it wasn't at all. There is no doubt in my mind that this generation has produced some of the best positive risk takers ever. What made us like this? We had self-determination, disappointment, success and responsibilities. Yes, we had after school activities like sports, band rehearsals and plays, but we didn't have to live on a minute-to-minute schedule like a fanatic.

I think it's fair to say that everything was safer; there was no 'edge'. Crime wasn't as bad, people could actually go to bed or take a bath without having to lock their doors. Now you really aren't safe in broad daylight in your own front room with the doors unlocked or locked! Yes of course it had its negatives too, like the cold war and knowing that you could be hit by a nuclear bomb anytime, any day. There would be times I would be walking in town with my long hair, jeans and denim shirt. Blue denim was as popular as ever, for shirts as well as jeans. Someone coming towards me would smile at me, acknowledging our connection. We really were that close and we didn't have to say anything, we just recognised each other's personalities. I feel for people who have never felt this, people who spent their time oblivious to real people and real feelings. Why couldn't they see, understand or appreciate each other?

Weekly parties were happening everywhere, and yes I put my hands up to attending most of them. I picked up quite a reputation for enjoying a good bash, and took to it like a duck to water. In fact I would be knee-deep in the goings-on at each party. Friday and Saturday nights were always about attending a good shindig, or trying to find one to gate crash if you hadn't received an invite. I wasn't overly bothered if it was a birthday bash, an engagement or a christening. The routine never changed. Halfway through the evening I would listen out in our local pub to try to get a name or address. Then I would arrive on the person's doorstep as if I had been expected. 'Hi Jim, I mean Pat, sorry it's Lucy isn't it?' Holding a large 'Party Seven' can of beer that provides for eight people, clearly displayed that I was going to be an accommodating guest. I've now learnt that the beer should have gone in the fridge for everyone. 1971 onwards were extraordinary years of discovery and change for me; I called it the practice run into the new decade. All the things I used to do when I was much younger no longer held any interest for me, I had moved on. Many changes, events and attitudes defined this time, and became a culture called the 'Me Decade.' I was taught to be thankful for what you had because no one was promised anything for the next day.

Chapter Seven

Glam Rock

Glam rock had arrived and ticked all of the boxes. People pretty much wanted the same thing as those who came before them: a happy life. Pop stars wore make up, had tanned bodies and wore six inch platform boots. These bands were having fun and didn't seem to be taking themselves too seriously. They were nothing like some of the bands that came along in later years. I know everybody gets a bit down sometimes, but some musicians made a career out of it. Take a look at Morrissey from The Smiths, or Ron Mael who never spoke and played keyboards for Sparks. I didn't know it at the time, but I was prepared for the take-off of glam rock. It seemed to happen overnight, suddenly the charts were full of songs with a weighty beat and catchy lyrics.

One of my favourite music shows in the 70s, first aired on the BBC, was *The Old Grey Whistle Test*, hosted by 'whispering' Bob Harris. Bob had his finger very much on the music pulse. This programme would acknowledge new bands and solo artists, and give them a fair share of airplay. On a Sunday I would chuck down my roast dinner and barely finish before scraping back my chair to dash into the front room to listen to Radio One. If you really liked a song, you would wait until it was played on the Top 40 countdown, and then put your cassette tape recorder up to the radio speaker and press record.

I would listen to the Top 40, flicking from one station to another. DJ Alan Freeman ('Fluff') would be bumbling his way through interviews with Led Zeppelin's Jimmy Page who would then rock out his famous ballad, 'Stairway to Heaven'. I was in awe of his guitar solo. Freeman became one of the voices of rock on Radio One, and had many listeners following him. Likewise with John Peel and Janice Long. Peel would play one whole side of an album so you got to really know the band's music before you decided to purchase it. He was an icon and known for his obscure and utterly crazy taste in music. He would spin vinyl at the wrong speed by accident, and there would be regular bouts of quiet air time when he went off to make cups of coffee. He certainly gave bands their big breaks, including T.Rex and The Undertones.

Top of the Pops was a regular family viewing on a Thursday evening from every sofa in Britain, starting promptly at 7pm. The Top 20 countdown was a huge thing. It took many more sales to make a number one hit record in those days. It felt like some of the good stuff of the 60s was actually filtering out to everyone else in the 70s. However, I do feel that this was the decade when music really did change. Music of today is always built upon its predecessors; that is where the 70s have built their reputation. So many of today's musicians will happily point to their inspirations and many steer directly back to this time. Back then music had so much diversity, from light hearted and happy sounding rock songs, to passionate experimental progressive music. It was made mostly by people who loved it and were gifted, rather than the formula stuff tossed out these days in the name of profit and fame. I loved, and still do, emotional songs with really strong lyrics. I can remember times during the mid-70s just lying on my bed listening to songs like 10cc's 'I'm Not in Love' and Procol Harum's 'Whiter Shade of Pale'. Sometimes bands would come along with a song so perfect, you would wonder how it hadn't been written before. Let's face it, music is the backdrop to most people's lives. It was a very electrifying time.

There seemed to be no end of music venues; just about every other pub had a live band on every other night. Of course, Barry White was a no-go! Unless you went out for a night at the Bodmin Jail Club and wanted to smooch the night away. For me, I preferred the Drum Major Pub situated in Bodmin, listening to brilliant local live bands such as The Gin House (Dick Ginn and Alan Hodge), Liberty Wolf, and not forgetting Saffron. This is when I really commenced my long lasting love affair with night life. Both Alan and Dick went on to have successful careers in their own right. Alan sadly died of a brain tumour in 2006, and Dick Ginn died in 2017. Every year Bodmin Town will hold a concert named 'Alstock' in Alan's memory. This annual concert is organised by his family and his close friends.

Music of the 70s didn't belong to anyone over 40 years of age; it belonged to us as teenagers. There were three types of music: disco, glam rock and rock. Classic rock was ushered in by the breakup of the Beatles in the first year of the decade. From that point on, several different sub-styles of rock began to come onto the scene, exemplified by Pink Floyd, Genesis, Queen, Led Zeppelin and Deep Purple.

I bagged glam rock straight away. It made me feel alive, positive and, I believe this was one of the reasons glam took off like it did. It demonstrated to me that life didn't have to be tedious, that music and fashion didn't have to have a deep meaning, that life was bright and there to be enjoyed. I was into Slade, T.Rex, the Sweet, and Steve Harley's 'Make Me Smile (Come up and see me)' on *The Cockney Rebel*. These bands certainly caused a flurry of activity. People were saying that the biggest problem with rock at this time was that it was boring. It makes you wonder if glam rock positioned itself as a backlash against the rock mainstream of the late 60s, on the periphery of society and rock culture. Glam rock was an almost entirely British phenomenon that became wildly popular during the first half of the 70s. It was fairly simple, crunchy guitar rock put across with outrageous theatricality.

Glam rock effectively began with T.Rex's 1971 hit album *Electric Warrior*, but 1972 was its real breakthrough year: T.Rex consolidated its popularity with the album *Slider*; David Bowie released his classic *Ziggy Stardust* album. Bowie and Bolan were rock's quirky couple. Mott the Hoople sang, 'My brother's back at home with his Beatles and his Stones, We never got it off on that revolution stuff' on *All the Young Dudes*. Glam emphasized outrageously flamboyant fashions: platform shoes, glittery costumes, garish make-up plastered on the faces of its male performers. Alice Cooper exploded onto the stage with his extravaganza theatrical show leaving people blown away by all the make-up and snakes. 'No more teachers, No more school.' Following behind would be The Sweet, Roxy Music and Slade. I would always be clutching a bag full of vinyl to play whenever and wherever possible. The music of the 70s was just awesome; people are still mixing and dancing to these hits to this day. However, others would argue that it did not take long for the public to see the insignificance and commercialisation in glam rock. John Lennon famously described glam rock as simply 'rock and roll with lipstick on.'

Once my parents had left the house for work each morning, I would crank up the sounds with T.Rex's 'Metal Guru', 'Telegram Sam' and 'Get It On'. This band would be strutting their Electric Warrior stuff on every stage across Britain. This was Marc Bolan, leader and visual symbol of the band T.Rex. Bolan took great delight in turning teenage bubble gum rock into confectionary glam rock sound bites. His boogie hit machine would get up to full steam, kicking those hits out one after another. So what if Bolan was going on about his cork screw hair, lizard leather boots, gutter-gaunt gangsters and sprinkled fairy dust. Loopy nonsense poetry maybe, but he was a charismatic master of a three minute pop song powered by his warm electric guitar.

My 70s black Phillips stereo record player took a daily thrashing from both speakers; I would change my stylus every three weeks. If the record was warped or skipped across the tracks, I would Sellotape a penny on the end of the stylus arm, it would then play. Neighbours would hear me pounding out Suzi Quatro's 'Can the Can', 'Put your man in the can, honey. Get him while you can.' The ultimate piece of kit that most people wanted was a music centre. This was a record player, cassette player and radio combined. They were becoming mainstream. In the summer I would hang the speakers out of my bedroom window and give it all. I would stack up to six records at a time and listen as they were lowered down and played through in order. I purchased my stereo from my friend's parents' Freemans' catalogue, paying it off at 50p a week. This was the norm back then.

I kept my albums right next to my bed, the most inspiring ones were placed neatly at the front. The obscure ones with the best sleeve covers, Bowie, Roxy Music and Black Sabbath. I would be drooling like Pavlov's dogs at the thought of purchasing the next Led Zeppelin album. Surely this would impress any girls coming in and flicking through my collection. At first it was all about purchasing singles but as months went by I started to get interested in albums. My oldest brother was also heavily into music, so his taste filtered down to me. I didn't really like a lot of his taste in music however, years down the road it clicked with me. Ah, so this is Fleetwood Mac, The Yes and Alan Parsons. Every Christmas I would give my parents, brothers, sister, uncles and aunties a list of albums I would most like for presents. 1972 was a winner, when I received T.Rex with *The Slider*, Status Quo with *Piledriver*, and Deep Purple's *Machine Head*. I would spin these albums whilst playing Haunted House, Operation and Buckaroo with my brothers. Mum and dad would be playing Mouse Trap with my sister.

A single (45 inch record) was roughly about 50 pence and LPs (long players) around £2.99. Low budget albums were also around at the time. Music for Pleasure and K-Tel records, costing £1.99. However, it was never the original artists singing. Posters of Slade, Bolan, Bowie and the Beatles were plastered on my bedroom walls. You would receive free plastic singles with every music magazine that you purchased. This was the time of bubble gum cards, tank tops, glam rock, woodchip wallpaper, *Coronation Street*, Clive Dunn singing 'Grandad', *Dad's Army*, Radio Luxembourg, Sunday Top 40 show, stamp albums, five shilling notes, Butlin's and Pontins holiday resorts, platform shoes, Ford Escort, Cortina and Capri cars, *The Topper* and *Beano* comics, Green Shield Stamps, The Fonz and *Happy Days*, the Harlem Globetrotters, Concorde's first supersonic flight, the PG Tips chimp adverts, *Kojak*, Space Hoppers and the Littlewoods catalogue. My little sister would pull along her Fisher Price phone and her dog with the springy tail. I can remember how disappointed she was that Santa had not bought her a Fisher Price record player with plastic grooved records.

We only had three television channels: BBC1, BBC2, and ITV. There was no 24-hour television; we watched all the stations in black and white. If I remember correctly, BBC2 only aired for part of the day, showing a still picture of a girl with long hair the rest of the time. Our first second hand television had a faded picture due to the tubes slowly burning out. I can still remember the occasions when people came to the house to visit. 'Where are the kids?' they would ask my mum. 'All four are under a blanket watching television to get a better picture.' She would reply. For me, children's television was a wonderful experience that I really looked forward to. I often wonder if it was made even more so because of the short viewing opportunity.

There were no remote controls back then. Can you imagine having to change the channel by turning a button to tune into BBC1 and forever getting up to readjust the aerial and contrast? Well we did! The only way to stop the picture from rolling was to give the television a good whack. The conversation was always on the same level at school the following day, as everyone was watching the same programs. It would be about *The Waltons*, *Little House on the Prairie* or *Crossroads*. Unlike now where we have 300 channels! TV was good and entertaining back then, it didn't separate family living in the way that it often does today. It was a treat to purchase a Vesta curry, or fish and chips in newspaper with scratchings, and eat off trays watching our favourite programmes on Saturday evenings.

A lot of things were invented during the 70s. This decade brought new experiences that our grandparents could barely have imagined. The floppy disc, food processor, video cassette player and word processor, video games, disposable lighters, ink-jet printers, push through tabs on drink cans, cartridge players, CB radio, calculators, cassette recorders, cassette tapes and the Walkman. All of this gave me a taste of what was going to change in the future.

I can remember not having a phone in the house. I would stroll to the local red phone box, after 6pm because it was cheaper, and wait for my friends to ring me. I must have looked weird standing around waiting for the public phone to ring. But this was quite normal back then. I would shove the coins into the slot when the pips went. Sometimes the money got jammed, and then as you finally managed to push it in, the other person on the line had hung up! No one collided into you on the street because they were babbling into a mobile phone or texting. Nowadays, almost everyone over the age of ten seems to own a mobile phone. Telephones back then were a status symbol that only the middle class would own.

It seems like yesterday when we bought our first washing machine. We all sat on the floor and watched it go round for one full load. This was fascinating at the time. All that was missing was a bag full of popcorn and a bowl of ice cream. One device that we all treasured was my brother's new polaroid camera. The chance to pose for a photo then wait minutes for the completed printed product to shoot out the side was just awesome. Before that, capturing memories meant pressing the button and taking the film into our local shop to be processed, waiting for ever and ever to actually view the result. One of the most exciting new technology events in our house was the overdue arrival of a VHS video recorder. Never before had we had the luxury to view pre-recorded films or programmes. We had been stuck with our three channels and all of a sudden a whole new world opened up for us all. A jaunt to the local video rental shop in the town to select a film made way for the new weekend evenings. Everyone was excited about this new technology, especially my dad and oldest brother.

My pride and joy was my vast collection of albums and singles. In other words, I was a vinyl junkie. It wasn't a bad collection if you consider that I was only young and totally aimless. My weekly read would be the *New Musical Express*, *Melody Maker* and *Sounds* music papers. In the middle of each paper was a free poster of a pop star. From that point on I would never be without a music paper or music magazine. Nor would I be without my headphones thrashing my pierced ears. As I write I have just been to see The Sweet, Slade and 10cc perform in Torquay, Fowey and Truro. Obtaining autographs from the Sweet members was a real bonus for me, having followed the band throughout my teens. They would become some of the national rock music pioneers who took every continent by storm for more than four decades.

The original Sweet were a classic glam rock band, who brought neutral looks and crunching guitar sounds to the crowds, and spent over three years in the UK charts alone. They have sold over 55 million records, including their number one hit 'Blockbuster'. They have had 34 number one hits worldwide and still play to sell out audiences throughout the world. The Sweet took visual appearances to the extreme, wearing glitter, excessive make-up and loud coloured clothes. That same week I met and thanked 10cc's Graham Gouldman for the amazing music that 10cc have delivered over the years, in fact decades. Graham and the band then signed their new disc for me, I was made up. Two bands in one week!

The one thing I was starting to notice back then in the 70s was that everyone was spending a good deal of time listening to music and talking about the history of artists. I found all kinds of music very relaxing and found it a way of leaving a busy, maybe bizarre day. I guess I am saying it was escapist stuff. In my opinion the best material came out in the 60s, 70s, and 80s. Record shops like 'Sounds' (Simon and Neil) George Ellis, and Marshalls (all based in Bodmin) were places where people could meet and listen to tracks together, somewhere where we didn't have to leave the premises once we had purchased our favourite artists.

Most record stores would have booths installed with stereo headphones so that you could listen to an album before paying for it. Buying an album wasn't just a quick outing to the record shop; it was an event, a huge event. There was nothing more exciting than purchasing a new album by my favourite artist, then ripping off the plastic wrapper. The album cover almost as thrilling as the music on the record. I would read the dedications and of course the lyrics as I listened over and over again. I wanted to feel what those had written felt, and interpret their words in a way that would help me to hook up to them. I do feel that music adjusts our moods whether listening to it or playing it.

People would take music more seriously than many other things in life. It was part of the way we defined ourselves, like the clothes we wore, the way we presented. We spent hours talking about our favourite bands and chosen music. Today most people surf the internet and download their favourite music. The back end of the 70s produced some excellent bands; their sound was completely different to what we had heard at the beginning of the decade. This I doubt will ever be repeated again. Sadly, the music industry has mourned the passing of some great solo musicians while some bands simply split up and went their own ways. 2016 was clearly a very sad year, losing so many well-known, talented artists. David Bowie RIP.

Chapter Eight

My First Real Job

In the summer of 1976 the weather was scorching and broke all the records. I was well tanned, and I mean brown. Some people thought they were living in California. In fact, the heat wave was so extreme there were water shortages over the entire country. In some areas people had their water supply turned off for most of the day to conserve water. Hosepipe bans were enforced across the country. A truly golden summer during which all parts of the UK basked in record hours of sunshine, temperatures soared above 30 degrees for at least a month, and the grass was absolutely brown. I can remember the ground cracking and the tar on the roads melting. It seemed to last forever; day after day of endless sunshine, long balmy summer evenings without a breath of wind to cool you down. I would pay someone to release a CD set of summer 1976 hits. The manufacturers and distributors of sun cream couldn't keep up with the demand. The humidity was breath-taking and people crowding around any shade to try and get some relief from the heat. The Prime Minister, James Callaghan, was forced to appoint a minister for the drought.

My memory of this summer was eternal sunshine; I never saw a single cloud. There was music, happiness and freedom, I was without a care in the world. Whatever happens in the future, at least I have memories of these endless days with blue skies. I had happy people around me having good times. No one, but no one can fleece that from you! It was a time when ordinary people felt that they could do something, maybe not change the world but we felt that our voices were being heard. Britain was going through a time of anarchic creativity. News was breaking through about a movement called punk with edgy names, a sound that was angry, vibrant and fast. Being laid back just wasn't any longer an option – you had to be angry.

Punk had made anything seem possible. Key elements of punk were ripped jeans, torn t-shirts, spikey haircuts, and worn and torn leather jackets.

Safety pins became nose and ear jewellery. To be a punk you needed to have a flung together, poverty look. Most people though were just looking for another way to vent their frustrations. The Sex Pistols' Johnny Rotten was asked what he wanted to do about the UK; he replied, 'Let's make it worse'. He later said that he had to put a stop to the 70s, because 'Someone had to'. In an interview the following week he said, 'Take your flares, and your 60s and shove them where the sun doesn't shine'. Punk rejected everything that had gone on before. This whole attitude kicked the doors open for a whole heap of new sounds to come through. Then in the middle of all this, enter Paul McCartney in full Fab-Macky-Wacky thumbs up. His band Wings came from nowhere with the mega hit single 'Mull of Kintyre' and went straight to number one! Yes, I bought it!

The new reality was anarchy in the UK, and a bitter cold winter which was named the Winter of Discontent due to the strikes. There was a three-day week when we ate cold meals by candlelight due to the power cuts which would go on for hours and hours. The only thing you could do was to retire to bed and keep warm. I would lie in bed working out all the things I would have to re-set when the electricity came back on. On several occasions, I recall the house turning completely black without any warning. My parents would rush around looking for the candles. The power cuts were a novel way to spend evenings. It was exciting for us when we were teenagers. Inconvenience would bond us together even more. The strikes were unbelievable and world famous. Then, in 1975, Margaret Thatcher was elected to the leadership of the Conservative Party. Thatcher was labelled the 'Iron Lady' and stood proud by this. Change was on the way. People asked many questions like, 'Would a female Prime Minister be more sensitive?' I remember watching news coverage of Margaret Thatcher washing the dishes in a member of the public's house, telling Britain that she understood the concerns of the everyday housewife.

The troubles in Northern Ireland dominated the headlines. A number of high profile mainland bombing campaigns in the mid-70s threatened London and major British cities. Peace in Northern Ireland seemed a distant hope at the time. Inflation was rocketing sky high; people were buying their own council houses. Green Shield stamps were everywhere in the Britain of the 70s. If you bought your groceries at certain shops the retailer gave you stamps to stick in a book. Once you had collected enough you could exchange the books for gifts. I went out and bought new sounds: Sham 69, The Sex Pistols, The Stranglers, The Jam and The Clash.

It was also the year that I eventually secured a full-time job at a large discount shop called 'Julian's Cash and Carry' based in Bodmin, at the old

Barracks, I really enjoyed working there. This was my first job, there was no application form and I had very little background knowledge in this area of work. I knew that I was very lucky as unemployment was high. Finding any job was a tough call in the strike-torn days of the 1970s. I knew deep down that I had so much potential to do more, but I had to go with it because work was work. The one thing I didn't want was to become another unemployment statistic. Turn up at the dole office, sign on the line, play the game, look unhappy then leave with your dosh? I grew up with a strong work ethic and struggle so much with those who are capable of working but don't. It's called 'milking the system'. In fact, it's stealing. Call it what you want, pocketing, embezzlement, thieving, it's all the same! In my book, if you have a pulse then you go to work.

This job gave me a sense of purpose and taught me key lessons about the world of work: that you cannot be cocky, cannot be late, that you had to speak clearly and listen. I slipped into the role with ease, kept my head down and worked hard. Day by day I was taught customer care, how to work under pressure, ways of working in a busy team, how to use my initiative, take responsibility, and improved my numeracy skills. Okay, the latter was a bit of a struggle.

Years later I would understand that working in a shop doesn't make you uneducated or unambitious. Just because a person spends their day in a shop rather than an office, ward, classroom or bank doesn't mean they are incapable of working in these areas, they have just made a choice not to. It needs to be understood that people really do want to work in this area; they have made a career out of it, and they enjoy it. This job gave me a wage with which I bought my first motorbike, a Honda CB 250 registration SAF 897M. My bike was my pride and joy. When I passed my bike test I was hardly at home, taking full advantage of my first taste of real independence. Was this the best thing that I had ever owned? Once off the road and into a field I would open the throttle right up, 'Hey look guys, no hands!', whistling a happy tune and smiling as I passed them all. And then, 'Hey look guys no hands or feet', swaying from side to side, and then as I came around the corner, 'Hey look guys no teeth!'

With my new bike I felt that I was automatically signed up with the Bodmin local bike club which made me very happy. A group of us who had been together for a long time, shared the passion of motorbikes. This was my life for a few years. Talking to our opposition – the ones on scooters – and diluting any secrets we had was unthinkable, so we just ignored them. But, I would have loved to have worn the clothes that they wore. I certainly wasn't one of the beard and sandal brigade. What we went through is a book in itself and not written yet. I would have to bring my closest friends on board to help me write it. It would document the times of my youth, my personal times, our times. I was lucky; I always felt that I could speak to my mates back then rather than them closing down on me.

On the other hand, some of my mates of about the same age appeared to be let off lightly when the judge passed sentence. However, as time passed it was apparent that time had marked an individual effect on a few of them. In some ways it was the beginning of the end for some. By no means were any of them bad or criminals, just so young and bored out of their skulls. Anyone looking might think were quite innocent. The smiles, nice clothes, aftershave and good manners, remembering to say 'please' and 'thank you'. Under the surface we were rascals. Others would go on to say that we were random, creative, casual or aloof; we continued to wear are badges of rebellion. We would laugh, argue and fight, but at the end of the day we were a tight circle of friends. That's not to say that there weren't endless nerve wracking aftershocks when something had occurred. You would look out for your own and share what little you did had. My fear of my age exposure gradually disappeared as I approached my significant birthday, when I would become totally legit. Phew! The last two years had been a challenge for Roger, Rodney and Tommy who owned the Drum Major pub.

It goes without saying that there were always a group of people doing their utmost to get an invite into our delinquent mischievous circle. In later years some would never get their lives together properly again. For me I needed to go through all this fun and excitement. It fed into everything that I loved. When excitement kicks in, rationality all but goes out the window. Looking back this is what has made me today. I would never change any of this, why would I? It's only as years go by when you get older and wiser that you start to realise there is this bigger picture and each segment of life is only part of it. I certainly learnt some lessons that have stood me in good stead ever since.

Two of my close mates who had more or less the same background as myself have had gone on in life and succeeded in their own right. It was clearly demonstrated to me that they certainly had a vision of where they were going, and boy didn't they do it well. These guys were as sharp as cider apples, although I guess you could have called them a pair of wide boys at the time, but they had those regular light bulb moments. On reflection I sensed that they were as lost as me, it brought us closer. At the time these guys were an important part of what we were doing. A master of the sound bite and tuned in. Both older than myself, they were clued in and had the knowledge, skills, networks and resources to do so much. They also had the most fabulous motorbikes you had ever seen. Being privileged to ride as a pillion was a cool place to be. They would often be in my thoughts as I entered my career in mental health, what would they think of me? Once a biker, all the things we got up to and now a nurse? When I recently called both of the them, they were so proud of where I was at. Both were another kind of mentor in a different way.

The biggest wakeup call for me came some eight months into the job when a customer came into the shop asking to view a portable cassette tape recorder on the top shelf of my display. It's hard to believe now, but we all thought cassette tapes were the latest best thing going. 'No problem Sir'. I turned to climb a ladder we used for climbing to the top shelves when I heard an almighty crash towards the glass showcase cabinet. The customer had collapsed right in front of me banging his head on the display cabinet. Although I had immediately shouted to other staff for assistance, I felt helpless as to what more I could have done at this stage. Alfie Symonds, my manager was the first person to arrive on the scene; he had made his assessment and started CPR on the man whilst he was turning a shade of grey. It was a horrible situation as the man's family were present. Hours later I discovered that he had died instantly from a massive heart attack. This incident remained with me for some time and I guess looking back there was a lot of guilt that I could have done more.

Alfie (a retired charge nurse who had worked at St Lawrence's Psychiatric Hospital for a considerable number of years) spent a great deal of time talking this incident through with me and kept saying that I needed to look at a career in nursing. I kind of shrugged my shoulders knowing that he was probably right but not knowing how to go about it. He knew deep down that the death of this man had played on my mind; he was the first person on the scene when I shouted for assistance and was so professional. Alfie would continue to bring this subject of nursing up. My reply to that was, 'What me Alfie? Working in general nursing? Come on, I don't think so.' That would just make me feel squeamish I thought to myself. I remember thinking, what all the rigidity of hospital routine? Dispensing medication, testing urine, polishing bath taps, cleaning tubes, cleaning bedpans, writing in charts, immaculate bed making, taking temperatures, and serving meals, relentless. His reply was, 'No not general nursing, go for psychiatry, I have been there and it's a good career, I can see you doing this role.' I remembered just standing in the shop thinking about it. The psychiatric hospital was just up the road from us.

I had no doubt in my mind that Alfie's words were sincere, but I may also have convinced myself that this was in fact a role for me. I knew deep down that I wanted to combine work with some kind of study. I also knew that I had dipped out big time on education and I needed it badly. I found myself looking at things that I didn't understand or couldn't get the hang of and made it my mission to make sure I did understand. Once mastered, I started to really enjoy my job; I thought right away that work would be my way of making something positive out of my life. For me, there was no obvious turning point moment, but I instinctively felt that something good would come from this that would make a difference.

Several months down the road things were starting to feel more settled. I wasn't doing so badly on my own after all. It was like a flick of a switch, overnight I smartened myself up and became more tuned in. I was all set to push out into the big scary world. There is nothing anyone can do or say that can change the past. You can either stay stuck or move on. How we feel today may not be the same as the next day, or next week, or next year. You have new insights, views may shift, and they did for me.

Alfie was very supportive when I was making this crucial decision. On reflection I think his judgement was the deciding factor. In many ways you could say that Alfie had started to mould the foundation of my career. He was a great man and as a teenager I really enjoyed working with him in the shop. He was interesting and had a great sense of humour. Some days I would be rolling around on the floor with laughter. He would always have a jolly laugh and had accompanying bouncing shoulders. He was notorious for keeping people on their toes; well known for not letting anyone know what he was up to from one minute to the next. Truly a bag of excitement. I learnt so much from him. He had all those years of experience working in mental health, and this was what I was about to embark on. I had no idea at all that I would remain working in mental health for the next forty-one years. It was good advice coming from someone who knew me best and I gained a clearer head and had a more positive outlook on things. Alfie and his family are some of the very few people outside of my own family who played a massive part in my life; this will stay with me forever. My family often bring this up and what a compliment. Alfie then took two weeks annual leave to go off on holiday with his family. I said I would see him when he got back.

On 9 December 1980, the morning after my hero John Lennon was tragically killed, three of us were travelling up to London to see the band Queen play at Wembley, one of the saddest days for all of us. This was massive news right across the world. It was my first experience of the death of an icon and it hit me like a bolt out of the blue. The nearest memory of anything like this for me was in 1963 when my Mum informed us that President Kennedy had been assassinated. The thought of an ex-Beatle being shot dead was just incomprehensible. Politicians had been assassinated not musicians. The shooting at the star's New York home outraged the world. That this person was a fan, and someone who craved celebrity himself, only added to the chilling unreality of this horrendous moment. My Dad would say to me, 'Youth is about living and playing, not the untimely death of pop stars.'

Lennon back then was the voice of many people. He questioned so much in life and in return it seemed to give people permission to question so much more. Lennon's lyrics would become a handrail to assist me through those difficult times that we all encounter as a teenager. The news itself was shocking, violent and untimely tragic, throwing a spotlight on the senseless stupidity of it all. Lennon was not a god, but a brilliant musician. Queen played a blinding tribute on taking the stage entrance. This band certainly knew how to entertain an audience; nobody could strut down a ramp into the crowd quite like Freddie Mercury. The first two songs were dedicated to Lennon. London that day was in mourning. So was the world. It was a sombre day.

On returning from London I was still horrified at what had happened. Lennon was dead I kept saying to myself, 'How could this have happened?' I kept thinking about how the Beatles had always been my own personal influence, their lyrics a catalyst in where I was at. I was not long home when I decided to phone Alfie. He had given me the telephone number of where he was staying. Despite being on holiday, he liked to be kept up to date with any unexpected issues at work. Alfie knew I was a huge fan of the Beatles. I rang the number and waited for him to pick up the phone; I was not expecting to hear what I heard. His son picked up the phone and I was informed that whilst away Alfie had become unwell and had died. It was as quick as that. I remember being really shocked and upset and found this news really hard to digest.

Over the coming months there were deaths in our family too. It was a very dark time indeed; a blur of sadness, confusion, misery, and a total sense of emptiness. It felt like you were just drifting down the river with the currents. The last thing I wanted to hear at the time was how sorry people were, and I knew deep down that if I had connected with their sadness I would be a total wreck. Years later, in my counselling and cognitive behaviour (CBT) modules, I gained a greater understanding of how to deal with death and bereavement. It took a while to get over these deaths.

Not recognising it at the time, there was light at the end of the tunnel. It does get easier and clearer each day. However, the sadness never goes away when you have those quiet moments.

If there was something else career wise that I could have done, then this was the time I needed to do it. What I could not possibly know then was that I was ending a chapter of my life, but another vitally important chapter was about to begin. All of this started me thinking again about nursing; mental health nursing. I rapidly considered the advantages of becoming a nurse and when I get hold of an idea it has to come out. The point was that I was now beginning to think of a world beyond that of a shop assistant. At the time my oldest brother was a mental health student nurse working at St Lawrence's Psychiatric Hospital in Bodmin. My Dad was a charge nurse delivering training, having trained at Moorhaven Psychiatric Hospital in Ivybride in Devon. I would often ask my Dad and my brother what it was like working at the hospital, without letting on that I was interested in working there.

They were very positive in their feedback and would give me a run down on what their roles consisted of and the history of the hospital. Little did they suspect my next plan. Determined not to wait too long, I plucked up enough courage to write a letter to request an application form for a nursing assistant post at our local psychiatric hospital, and asked friends to check my spelling. With my hastily written application form I ran to the nearest post box and flicked it in, job done. Alfie would have been proud of me I thought to myself.

I always enjoyed Sunday dinners with my family. It was the one day of the week where all the family relaxed. However, this particular Sunday morning had been a bit of a nightmare. I had climbed onto the top of the kitchen cupboard to retrieve my last three cigarettes that I had stashed the night before, bringing the whole cupboard to the floor. I bounced off the kitchen worktop, did a figure of eight in the air; then landed on my head. I ended up being buried with the content of the cupboard on top of me! I was covered in flour, spaghetti, sugar and spices. Dazed and confused with cuts to my head, I eventually got up and swayed around with concussion. 'Great start to the day' I thought. Hours later, with cuts to my face, we eventually sat down as a family to eat our roast dinner. Mum would always cook us all a proper home cooked meal, but most of the desserts were bought from the local shop, ranging from ice cream, peaches and clotted cream, angel delight, or rice pudding from a tin can with a dollop of strawberry jam in the middle.

The 70s was a decade that saw a surge in convenience foods and no one really worried about whether or not they were good for you. We were a family who always sat around the table to eat; it was a chance to exchange news and updates on what everyone was up to. A time when if some of your food dropped off your plate when you were eating, you would just pick it up off the floor and give it a good old wipe, and stick it back in your mouth. Lovely. (Please don't start me off on the handkerchief and spit routine.)

Around the table we would discuss all sorts of daily activities, what we were doing in our day to day jobs, plans for the weekend, which person was seeing who, music, and so on. My young sister's eyes would slowly glaze over? Seconds later she would fall off her chair from complete boredom. The one thing we did share was our sense of humour and the house would be full of laughter. My parents always treated us as equals with opinions that were just as valid as theirs. They weren't envious or small minded. Having been the rebel of the family I sat thinking 'wait until you hear my news', and waited until there was a silent window to announce my intentions. I just knew what their reaction would be.

I waited a long time, the moment had to be right, the inside of my mouth was dry and It felt like I was crunching on two dry Weetabix. I took a deep breath, psyched myself up and began, 'I just want you all to know that I have applied for a nursing assistant post at the hospital, I am awaiting a date for an interview that is if I get short listed.' I counted to ten in my head and cringed whilst waiting for some feedback. Surely they wouldn't take me seriously. I had never shown any inclination that this was something that I wanted to do. It seemed uncomfortable bringing it up in my early nightmare teens.

I may have thrown my napkin on the floor for some sort of diversion, but when I got back up (which seemed like an age) silence had fallen around the table. I think they were waiting for me to say I was jesting, that I hadn't meant what I had said. I would have done anything at all that would help them all to breathe again! My Dad's face was an absolute picture, mouth ajar with a roast potato dropping back onto his plate. My brother spluttered his mouthful and nearly choked while my younger brother dropped the gravy boat splattering everyone within reach. My sister laughed so hard that a garden pea shot straight up her nostril. 'Are you serious?' she asked me, dislodging the pea with her finger. Mum just sat quietly in disbelief with the rest of the family, not saying a word. Their heads were going up and down like yo-yos. It was all so much like slow motion and if videoed, I'm sure it would have brought in a nice cheque from *You've Been Framed*.

Their facial expressions were unbelievable; their thoughts must have been 'What? You the rebel nightmare who brought so much adolescent disgrace to the family?' Now I need you all to know that I played this down (please, you must put your handkerchiefs away). There wasn't any malice in their facial expressions, but more humour. My family had never judged me and always supported me and praised the good things rather than criticising the bad things. I really did think that they thought I was having a bit of banter, that there was no truth in this whatsoever.

The truth was I so wanted to get this job. Once you have lost the momentum that has been so irresistible then there is no way of getting it back. Something was on the horizon, something really exciting. I was hoping that maybe this might be my first real job, after all the knock backs at school I felt really good. Isn't it bizarre how some things seem to come full circle? The way your life seems to drift along with no real set path, then something positive happens to you and you can trace that line that brought you there. Some six weeks later the letter arrived with a loud letter box slam. Sure enough it was an invitation to attend an interview in two days' time for the nursing assistant post at St Lawrence's Hospital. This suddenly shifted me into another gear, the first hurdle I thought to myself.

There were butterflies in my stomach on the evening before my interview, as I anxiously carried out a mental checklist to make sure I was equipped for my big day. I was stepping over the threshold into a profession that was going to consume my entire working life. The morning eventually came and off I went dressed in my best clothes. I had dug out my one and only suit. It was hardly a Carnaby Street style suit, but it would do. The last thing I wanted was to look like an unmade bed! People had never seen me in a suit before and they knew that I was making an effort; trying to cut the mustard. At the time my hair was homage to Paul Weller and Bruce Foxton of the band The Jam (a feather cut which was the in thing). This hairstyle was one of the longest lasting haircuts of the decade.

I remember bouncing along to the hospital grounds in the same manner that Liam Gallagher from Oasis does, my suit jacket draped over my shoulder and my family still looking on in disbelief and shouting out, 'Paul, we hope you've changed your pants!' It wasn't until I caught a glimpse of myself walking past the window of the West End café that I noticed that I still had my toothbrush hanging out of my mouth. On arrival I booked myself in at the main reception and was escorted to the waiting room. I sat there waiting in complete silence except for the deafening sound of my heart beating. I was called promptly and, checking my hair and the cuts to my face in the mirror and scanning for any zits, I sauntered in. I was then introduced and interviewed by Acting Senior Nursing Officer Mr Harold Vanderwolfe and Senior Nursing Officer Mr Kevin Hennely, both of whom I went on to have great respect for. 'Paul we have read your application form; it's come at a good time as we do have vacancies,' said Mr Vanderwolfe. They both tapped their fingers together in an approving sort of way. My knees were knocking together and we soon started to get a real rhythm going. In my head I started to sing Showaddywady's hit 'You Got What It Takes' I thought this was more than appropriate.

At the interview I was asked many questions, and my answers met all the criteria. It was in the forefront of my mind that I had quickly found some sort of common sense. I was very careful that I didn't trot my answers out too fast. Whilst Mr Vanderwolfe took the lead and chaired the interview; Mr Hennely sat just listening, writing and observing to see what kind of a person I was, and how I came across. He kept looking at his watch! Neither of them asked me where the cuts on my head came from. At the end of the interview, which lasted no more than half an hour, they asked me if I liked cricket. I was starting to doubt what I had on dress wise, and glanced down to see if I was dressed in white, my nerves having caused me to pick up the wrong clothes this morning. (Well it did happen on the milk round.) On the way out, I noticed a small television on a shelf showing a cricket match, and later discovered they were both cricket mad and played in the hospital cricket team.

I disliked cricket immensely, so I was relieved that they had left it there. The last thing on Earth I wanted was to be asked to join the St Lawrence's Hospital cricket team. I was very much aware that there was still a hierarchical system of nursing in power. There were many stories of petrifying and harsh sisters who controlled their staff like dragons, with grit and rods of iron. I was informed that if any staff member stepped out of line, they were immediately summoned to the office to be given a ticking off. Over the coming years, I would observe various staff members exiting the office looking dishevelled and exhausted.

I was relieved that I had got home on time to watch *The Two Ronnies*, and *Starsky and Hutch*. I wasn't so keen on *George and Mildred* or *Kojak*. Home life in the 70s still centred largely on the family. Most teenagers came home from work or school, did their homework, ate evening dinner with their parents, and then watched TV or went out. I waited for eight days before a letter arrived to say that I had been appointed to the nursing assistant post. They had found something in me that was by no means academic just then, but would interest me, and most importantly I knew that I could do because I was practical and had become an organised person.

What was quite unusual was the fact that the whole process seemed so natural.

I had a genuine grin, a split your face grin; the one that spreads from ear to ear. I was over the moon and started dancing around the house singing to a McCartney track, called 'With a Little Luck' from the London Town album. In the meantime, my family were looking in thinking, 'Oh dear, we are not quite sure where all of this is going to end up.' Me neither to be honest with you. Before the ink was dry on my contract, I took a long walk around the hospital grounds in order to orientate myself before my start date. What fascinated me the most was the fact that the hospital was a community. The patients had everything in front of them to assist them with their recovery. I walked the grounds feeling proud that I was now part of this establishment.

Accepting your past, whatever it may be, gives you a whole new outlook. Rather than dwelling on the past, it was about looking towards the future. The future would be better than what I had at the time. This really motivated me and the thought of bettering what I had gave me a real sense of purpose.

Chapter Nine

Everything Changes: St Lawrence's Hospital

I commenced my nursing career at St Lawrence's Hospital in Bodmin Cornwall on 17 November 1977 as one of 'Cyril Deacon's boys'. My work ethic comes from both of my parents. Most people knew my Dad who worked in the field of psychiatry for thirty-nine years. He was a Registered Mental Nurse (RMN).

It took courage to take positive risks and reject the bonds of fear, and there was no doubt in my mind that the road ahead would be a long and winding one that would be difficult at times. It wasn't going to be easy but that was fine. Taking control, leading the way, I started to change my destiny. My approach was always to decide how to get something done because failure was never really an option. I'm not a person who takes one step forward, and three steps back. Just like any new job the first day was always a bit nerve jerking. I had to work through the transition of being a novice to a new zone of territory. My very first post was as a nursing assistant on Kenwyn Acute Admission ward; my first charge nurse was to be the brilliant Pat Broderick.

Pat was a very experienced nurse; he was creative, well thought of, musically talented, and also a Morris dancer. Months down the road patients would slop their tea into their meals watching us do the Morris dance in the day room at their request. We had watched Pat dance on many occasions at events around Cornwall and he was good. We tried our best and would always get a round of applause. It gave all of us pleasure and entertainment too on a long day; we loved it.

Pat had that totally focused approach to everything. He was ahead of the game, and later worked his way up through the nursing ranks to management. He was incredibly inspiring and a good person to have as your leader. Most importantly, he made me welcome and at ease right from the first moment that I walked onto his ward. I had, and still have, total respect for him. I have always said that Pat was a role model for me. Pat had been a staff nurse for many years and was then appointed to a charge nurse. He was passionate and charismatic. The patients loved him and he would always be making jokes with them, never laughing at them but laughing with them. Fun and trust can be a powerful healer. When people are on the same wavelength it is so easy to work with them. In fact, you want to work with them all the time. Later on I was to discover that Pat had actually worked with Alfie over the years and what a coincidence that was.

Other mentors in my early career were the late Steve Davis, who was a star, the late Les Gerken, Lesley Maynard, Dave Tyrell, Dave Burgess, Pete Marlow and Dave Bowden. A good leader is someone whose team members will follow through to the end, in both good and bad times. They have confidence in that person, and their ability and knowledge of the job. As a leader you need to be enthusiastic; there is nothing as contagious as enthusiasm. A manager is someone who has patience, stamina, understanding, empathy, the ability to multi-task, works under pressure, motivated even when exhausted, and is conscientious about the work that they do.

I was made up on my first day walking through the main gates and as proud as ever, thinking, 'Well here it goes, a real job, a job for life if it all goes well.' The next few months were both memorable and intriguing to say the least. I was measured up for my grey suit and my six long white coats. I attended an induction week, and then it was all systems go. On the first day of the induction course we were taught all about confidentiality, that we were never allowed to divulge any information about patients, other nurses, certainly not about our personal life. The induction course was a real eye opener for me.

On my very first duty I was so keen that I was up at the crack of dawn; the first to arrive on the ward not really knowing what to expect. I am not quite sure why but for the next twelve years working at the hospital I would arrive on the ward before any of the other staff on our shift. I enjoyed greeting the night staff at 7am, setting up a tray of tea for the team coming on duty, turning the ward lights on and speaking to the patients who were just getting up. Working on the ward was tiring. It was a ward where twelve-hour shifts were worked, 06.55–20:05. It was tough; nursing is a twenty-four hour a day, seven days a week, fifty-two weeks of the year job. It's a round the clock, round the year service. Looking back now I wondered how we all got through these shifts.

As I've said, St Lawrence's Hospital was a community in itself; the patients had access to so much. Some of the ward's doors were locked and male and female patients were segregated. New medications and treatments were on the horizon. These new treatments also brought about huge changes in how patients were managed. Emerging medications made patients' lives less encumbered by severe side effects such as drooling and confusion that previously served to isolate and stigmatise. Long-acting forms of medications had been developed to help patients who were unable to manage having to take medication on a consistent basis. When I had arrived padded cells, strait jackets, cuffs and chains had all disappeared. This also included the surrounding walls. Patients who would have been securely locked up many years ago could now be seen walking freely in Bodmin's streets. Most of the emphasis was on treatment, security, prevention of patients escaping, prevention of injury to the patient or others, including the nursing staff, or damage to the hospitals property.

This was a time when it was seen as beneficial to provide most patients with suitable work roles. Before being admitted to the hospital, most patients had been working in jobs involving hard physical labour. It was desirable that most of the physically fit patients should be given work to suit their capabilities. Regular occupational therapy was also introduced. One of the main focal points of the hospital was the farm, where large numbers of patients would work daily, supervised by the nursing staff. Most of the food that went into making patients' meals was produced on the farm.

Back in the late 70s, other forms of work and activities would be assisting kitchen staff and domestics, putting away linen, boiler cleaning, wood chopping, basket making, sewing, printing, woodwork and repairing clothes. 'Bundles' were left to us nursing staff, who every day rolled a vest, pants and a pair of socks for each patient all ready for the morning. For carers, relatives and patients, the hospital began to lose its stigma as patients were no longer seen as locked away and forgotten.

Whether qualified or unqualified, nursing staff had to write a letter of request if they wanted to grow a beard, or needed to attend an appointment outside of their structured shift pattern which would alternate every three months. Our nursing officer, Mr Vanderwolfe, once came through the ward I was working on, took one look at me and flicked the back of my hair which was below my white coat collar. 'Mr Deacon, please get your haircut. You haven't put this in writing to me about growing it.' 'Yes Sir.' I replied. You had to stand if you were seated when doctors and nursing officers arrived on the ward.

My first few weeks working on Kenwyn Ward were a real experience. The whole idea of working with people who had mental health problems was now becoming a reality with me. Listening to people talk about this kind of work and then working on the wards were completely different. It took a good year to feel that I had settled in. It was my first nursing role and I was completely in awe of the team. They all knew each other well by now and at first I felt out of the loop. This changed and soon I was to feel at ease within this environment. I kept thinking to myself, well they all started at the same start line as me, so they must understand.

Over the years I would come across some fascinating people, they taught me a lot about life out there on the streets, mainly depression, substance abuse, violence and poverty. I enjoyed talking to people because they are all walking books. Sometimes I would only meet them once, but they would certainly make up a chapter. I am intrigued by the way we all live. When you meet someone new, what they represent can be written all over them. Some patients knew absolutely nothing about their past lives. They wouldn't discuss any of their emotions, when and where they were born, where they married or where they met, or what they did. Sometimes personal photographs played a huge part, helping them to open up and discuss some things.

Kenwyn Ward had twenty beds; the patients who were of various ages and were all male. It wasn't long before I was learning about all the different illnesses and treatments, a process which continued throughout my career. This included schizophrenia, bipolar disorder (formally called manic depression), dementia, anxiety disorder, self-harm, anorexia, depression and personality disorder. Years later I learnt about other treatments: medication, psychotherapy, group psychotherapy, electroconvulsive therapy (ECT), cognitive behavioural therapy (CBT), art therapy, and family therapy. It wasn't long before I had grasped the process that followed when someone was admitted either under a section of the mental health act, or as an informal admission: assessment, treatment, discharge and, in years to come, follow up of treatment. This all sounded easy, but it wasn't.

I wasted no time in constantly asking my colleagues questions, and Pat wasted no time in delegating tasks to his staff. He would say, 'Come on lads, it should only take you four minutes to make an empty bed.' Believe me; the beds were neatly made, including the traditional 45-degree hospital corners, the way I still make beds at home today! Student nurses would look at Pat waiting for the nod of approval. Row upon row of neatly made up beds stretched out before you in the large dormitory. I was clearly keen to learn and follow direction – keen to do anything that might prevent me from looking or feeling foolish. I knew that first impressions were important: it was about being punctual, polite, and courteous. I learnt to observe everyone and everything (even on off duty nights out!) It was a very busy day on the ward and I was still settling in. In my first week, we had a death on the ward and I kept thinking of the person who had died in front of me at Julian's Cash and Carry.

I started to go through all the bad scenarios that any mental health nurse goes through during their career. But every negative experience that I encountered was outweighed by the positive experiences. It's a longer-term sense of satisfaction at being able to help people when they are troubled. It became incredibly rewarding. I knew that nursing was going to be my route as a career and in time I would discover that this was in my blood. Now, this is all that I have ever known. I knew deep down that I knew nothing about this role. It's easy to find yourself out of our depth and at times, I would find myself on a ward that I did not have the skills for. In a way this was a good thing because too much confidence can be harmful. At times, like others, I struggled with some parts of the job. I was thrown into the deep end at such an early age, at the time I felt that this was not an ideal decision from the management. However, as time went by I felt that I had benefited from these decisions, as I gained a whole set of new experiences in a relatively short space of time.

Nursing staff were happy to sit on the side-lines and observe me trying to deal with the day to day confrontation with patients. Looking back, this was a good way of building those skills. There was so much to take in every day, mental health act sections, ward rounds, systems, processes, routines, different professionals, doctors, wards, and new patients as they were admitted. My head was screaming that my brain couldn't retain the amount of information I was expected to learn, and I wasn't even taking exams at the time. Little by little things started to come together. In years to come I was to specialise in various psychiatric settings including the personality disorder unit for the adolescent patients at Broadmoor Hospital. This was a ward that detained dangerous forensic patients.

It took some patients a long time to pluck up the courage to converse with me; as I was a new Kenwyn Ward staff member, some were suspicious. As one patient put it, I was a threat. One of the first patient conversations I encountered went, 'What the hell are you looking at?' Fair comment I thought, it wasn't much of a conversation, but at least there was an opening to work with. Our conversations would build over time, but I could see that he was struggling to cope with numerous conversations with the voices in his head, focusing on the demons, going from one topic to another. Diagnosed with schizophrenia, his voices were never pleasant. Before his hospital admission I had learnt that he had stopped taking all of his medication. This had brought on the voices and the hallucinations. Prior to his admission he became very paranoid, stating that the television was broadcasting messages into his head; the voices were telling him that the medication was poison, and not to take it. Taking medication helps patients to lead a fairly day to day routine within life. However, the patient may then think they are cured and no longer require medication. This can cause a relapse, as it did in this case.

Building a therapeutic relationship over time, he would become comfortable with me and would gain trust in me. I would no longer be an intruder who he feared. There were times when I felt quite vulnerable faced with a truly psychotic patient, imagining that what they saw was so real to them. With this particular patient, I learnt not to reinforce his beliefs that there were men in a white van parked outside the ward ready to kill him. Sometimes he would be screaming with fright and nothing that you did would calm him, medication would then be given to settle him. This is a very frightening state to be in for a patient and family members. I would observe on a daily basis their faces, scared and lost. They would later describe their situation as like trying to find some sort of order amongst the chaos.

They had no real thinking time because their reality was occupied with what was going on in their heads at that time. I really did take on board how powerful the brain was. To observe a young person tormented by thoughts in their head is truly terrifying. It's also disturbing to be informed by a patient that the voices are instructing him to kill you. After months of treatment he was discharged from the ward. He was such a nice man and you would never have guessed just how psychotic he had actually been during his admission. Observing your patient getting better, knowing that you are part of the team that is responsible for making that difference, is just unbelievably positive.

'You're a new member of staff,' said a patient heading towards me. 'You think you know how to nurse me? Is that the idea to help me? Go back home little one, you don't know anything, you're just a little boy who will end up getting hurt.' At the time I wasn't prepared for this razor-sharp comment. One of the staff nurses spent time in my break reassuring me that this was how the person presented when unwell. It occurred to me that there wasn't very much that would shock an experienced mental health nurse. I realised at this stage that I knew very little about this role. However, I certainly wasn't fazed by psychiatry, how could I be? I was ready for any new challenges that it would bring.

Mental Illness is more widespread than most people would think. The more severe mental disorders are schizophrenia, bipolar affective disorder and depressive illnesses. Mental illness is still associated with myths and misunderstandings. Those who have had mental health problems will still say that at times they have been stigmatised by society. Some see their presentation as disturbing and frightening. Tragedies in which members of the public had been killed by people with severe mental disorders have attracted the most horrendous headlines in the tabloid papers. We live in an increasingly violent society, but very few mentally ill people are in any way violent.

People who weren't working in this field of psychiatry would often say to me that mental illnesses are like any other, but this isn't true. When someone is physically unwell and presents certain behaviours, there is evidence in front of you that you can understand. However, it can be impossible to uncover the reasons as to why mentally ill people behave as they do. At times, the reasons are based on beliefs that are untrue; they claim to have experiences which appear to be either super or absurd. Over the years people have spoken about how mental illness is a frightening experience for them, saying that it can lead them to behave in an unpredictable and embarrassing way. Throughout my career I have nursed people with severe disturbed mental ill health. An admission to an acute inpatient unit or a psychiatric intensive care unit is an attempt to treat the person away from their familiar environment. This may be because the person cannot or will not stay at home, or because they are refusing treatment.

These admissions can be a way of reducing life threatening situations which could include attempting suicide. People are closely observed on a ward where staff can undertake an assessment of what those difficulties are. It is a neutral environment in which to assess and commence treatment. It is acknowledged that people do better if their centred care is the responsibility of a named nurse over a period of time, with the emphasis on patient choice, empowerment and collaborative relationships. A common theme that I came to see, was that people with schizophrenia would stop taking the medication that stopped the voices in their heads. Paranoia would be a common presentation. Voices would tell them not to take their medication as it was poison and they would end up flushing it down the toilet. Television or radio broadcasting would send messages to them.

I remember walking into the day area of Kenwyn Ward where all the patients sat, talked and watched television. 'Hello my son, bless you,' I heard as an elderly gentleman came towards me. 'Thank you for coming to see me today.' I wasn't sure who this was being directed at. I turned around thinking that his relatives were behind me and would guide him towards them, they weren't. As he hugged me and then held my hand he said, 'Now come and tell your old Pa what you have been up to all week.' This was all part of the job, something I would often observe and get used to as time went on. Many a time I would walk away with porridge or jam smeared on my cheeks after receiving a slobbery kiss.

So many patients that I nursed were so desperate to be heard and understood, and just needed some time spent with them. For some patients the wards would offer comfort, but most people found this hard to cope with. Hours later another patient would approach me, 'Gotta light nurse?' When I took my lighter out of my pocket I looked up and he had a page from the *Cornish Guardian* newspaper rolled up and hanging out of his mouth with two strands of tobacco at the end. Do I light this? However, things had certainly moved on since *One Flew over the Cuckoo's Nest*.

Observing some patients on their first admission, you would immediately sense that their past was one of pain and isolation. There were no real positive role models or mentors in their lives. Mentally unwell, homeless, broke, cold and living in a dingy, dirty room. There would be no curtains, no carpets; some would sleep on a sofa that smelt of damp. I visited many a home like this when patients had gone AWOL or had been discharged from the hospital. One patient said to me, 'Paul, we are a functioning dysfunctional family most of the time, when things are good it's pure magic.' However, there wasn't such a thing as a golden happily ever after for everyone. There was a lot of banter between patients and staff, and very long days for all of us. Our day started at 6:55am and finishing at 8.05pm. Despite this the humour would roll in, 'Nurse, I think I'm turning into an apple!' 'Don't worry we'll get to the core of this.' 'Nurse, I keep seeing double', 'Okay have a sit down on this chair', 'Which one?' 'Nurse, I think I'm a bell on a bike', 'Okay take these tablets and if they don't work give me a ring.' 'Nurse, I think I have got symptoms of déjà vu', 'I'm sure I saw you yesterday!' Last one, 'Nurse I think I'm a snooker ball', 'Okay I'll see you in a minute, just join the cue.'

I remember so vividly the time I was taught how to test urine for sugar, ketones and blood. I was taken into the wards clinical room. The staff nurse had all the glass tubes lined up along with the dip sticks. He took me through the process and then asked me to do the same and document my findings on the relevant chart. I did exactly what he had taught me and gave the readings over. He took a look through and said, 'No Paul, that's not the right reading, if in doubt do this.' He then picked up the tube and drank it! Swirling it around in his mouth, I was completely shocked! I couldn't believe what I had just witnessed. After spitting the urine out he started to write down his findings. It was only seconds after when everyone started laughing outside the clinical room that it all fell into place. This was apple juice and a regular bit of fun with any new staff member.

This story always makes me laugh every time I think of it. The patient also found this highly amusing. We will change his identity and call him Joe. He was having real problems using his bowels and complained of chronic stomach ache. I said it might be worth raising this with the doctor once he arrived on the ward. The patient agreed and waited at the entrance of the ward for the doctor to arrive. Later on in the morning he was seen in the ward round as discussed; the doctor diagnosed constipation and prescribed salts. The patient agreed, took the salts and then waited for some hours for a result.

Whilst I was in the corridor seeing to another patient, Joe ran past me heading towards the toilet, knocking all the dining room chairs over. Twenty minutes passed so I thought I better go and see how he was getting on. I ran down to the toilet area. 'Joe, how are you getting on?' I shouted. 'Not very good Paul, the door is unlocked, can you come in and give me a hand?' 'Okay' I replied, 'I'm coming in.' As I opened the door I was presented with faeces all over the walls, even the ceiling. 'Goodness gracious' I called out as I held my nose and started to heave. 'What kind of salts did the doctor prescribe you?' I shouted out loud. Joe replied, 'Somersaults!'

The hospital had a social club (the Glamour Social Club) where patients would take the opportunity to relax and socialise. This had full size snooker tables, dart boards, a canteen, films, bingo, competitions and parties at Christmas and Easter. The hospital also had their own radio station called 'Radio Beacon'. Staff would take it in turns to spin the vinyl of patients' requested music or read out messages. Each ward had their own speaker system for patients to keep in touch. There was a monthly magazine put together by patients which was called *The Beacon*. It contained hospital news, announcements and forthcoming events. This kept everyone up to date with what was happening within the hospital.

I always intended to visit other parts of the hospital whilst on duty, but I didn't have time to walk around the other wards to see what they were like as things were much too busy.

There was so much to take on board in the early days, and I carried around a pocket size notepad. I even wrote down the advice of one staff nurse, 'Listen young Deacon, when you make a tray of tea for everyone you need to swish the tea pot around with hot boiling water first. Always keep your words rather sweet, you never know when you might have to eat them.' Had I said something? I nodded my head, keeping a serious expression on my face. Others might have been offended by this but I took a different view. I really wanted to do it all right but I made blunders on the way, the important things was to use the experience to ensure that mistakes were avoided in the future. What was different now from my school days, was the fact that if I did make a mistake I wasn't waiting for 'Deacon come here now!' There was no putting me on the platform to ridicule. There was no cross examination. There was no pointing the accusing finger, or rigorously looking through my school bag for evidence of wrongdoing!

The nursing terminology everyone used sounded like titles of obscure rock band albums. I was still a little bit wet behind the ears, the youngest new anchor on the ward. Right from the onset, I loved the energy and unpredictability that came from the ward environment. I was finally working with people I could learn from, people I could look up to, and people who took things seriously.

Good lessons were learnt early, but they were never easy. I quickly learnt the essence of good team work, people working together where everyone gets on. To stay clear of any gossip and not get involved, not to talk to each other over patients as it is unprofessional. Never assume that they cannot hear what is being said. I loved working with people who had a great sense of humour and who were committed. Everyone signed up to the ward's philosophy and were seen out on the floor. It was about being visible.

What I was to learn later on in my career is that there were times when it could be so hard, especially when there was a suicide on the ward involving a young person. As a nurse no matter how professional you are, no matter how many times you had seen and dealt with this before, it was impossible not to be moved emotionally. For all of us living and well, who were able to endorse life and have a laugh and have fun, to see a person of a similar age to myself who had always wanted all of this in their life but whose young life had been taken. No matter what observations were put in place to monitor the safety of that person, some patients would be determined to kill themselves. They would find a way. When a tragedy occurs, and it is such a tragedy, you develop a strong sense that life is fragile and we don't always spend enough time being grateful for what we have got. The fact is all these wonderful things can vanish within minutes. I have witnessed and dealt with this awful time. It really makes you think. Most of us take it for granted that we can leap out of bed in the morning, brush our teeth, and go off and do what we do.

I'm sure all of you out there that work in mental health will agree that this type of nursing is such a unique career. Even today, humour must play a huge part in our day to day business. How else can one tolerate the insults, the verbal and physical abuse that is frequently thrown at us as nurses if we can't laugh them off? Nurses are expected to maintain a strong cheerful demeanour at all times; keeping their emotions tight. As nurses, we were present when serious things happened to patients. Accidents, violence and death are but a few of the issues that have to be dealt with on a regular basis. We would also work closely with families, making critical decisions, and deal with ethical dilemmas on a day to day basis. Yes it can be challenging and rewarding to help patients through these difficult times, but it can also be psychologically exhausting. Working with patients at some of the most vulnerable moments of their lives made some days difficult; we had to take steps to ensure that stress didn't affect our professional and personal life.

The combination of good planning and passionate staff is exactly what you need to have a successful team. It's all part of the skills that makes a ward team stand out from others. For some it would seem quite traumatic when there were changes with staff, and rotation to other wards took place every three months, known to everyone as quarters. There was a lot of sense in this as the rotation allowed the nurses to use their transferable skills. A fixation on retaining people when you were essentially trying to change things doesn't always quite work. They simply represent history while others are busy building and implementing the future. For those that really wanted to be there it was a case of looking after them and nurturing their skills.

Lengthy hospital life tended to skew the patients' perception of what nurses actually did. On Kenwyn Ward, patients would see everyone running around dispensing medication, assisting with hygiene, taking phone calls, dealing with incidents and patients would still pose the question, 'Haven't you ever thought about working in a real hospital or going off to train to become a real nurse!' Patients on the acute admission wards could see when another patient's needs were greater; they would have a front row view of real life issues. One minute they could be in conversation with staff or another patient, the next minute the whole ward had erupted. The emergency alarms would go off and we were required to head towards some unfolding incident not quite knowing what we would find when we got there. All of this was guaranteed to increase the flow of adrenalin.

There were times when I would listen to a colleague going on and on about conditions of their contract, the pay, the hours, how cold it was, how hot it was. I couldn't care less at the time, surely it had to be just getting your head down and get on with the job that you were employed to do. The hours working on a ward would go on forever and ever and would blot out any of this kind of thinking for me. The greatest downfall of all is when people became so wrapped up in negativity. I have truly gone out of my way to remove myself from people who are so negative. It was like on-going bitterness. I would find and spend time with those who were positive. Some people would just revel in negativity, in negative criticism of others, even those who were trying to make a difference on a day to day basis.

Some people would be busy with nothing, all getting wound up about nothing, being bored with all the nothingness in their individual lives. Gossiping and going on and on about nothing, nothing at all. My mission was to stay clear of any gossip tree-shaking, and the pointing of fingers. Too much drama, stirred by the trivial was my thinking. Focus on what you have, not what you have lost. I was always trying to put a positive spin on the minority who were this way inclined. Why would you waste so much time and energy on petty tittle-tattle? I found it interesting to note that just because my colleagues wore the same uniform as me didn't mean that we had anything in common, for example external interests.

Over the next few months it was all about gradually getting to know each other within the team. We were all from different backgrounds. It's no different to any other professional environment; working in hospital wards you have to learn how to work with all sorts of different personalities, even those that may be difficult or unpleasant to be around. We have all been there over the years, whilst reading this you will have by now conjured up a face or two. General nurses would look puzzled about the fact that I was working in mental health. 'This isn't a real nursing role,' they would say to me. 'There is no washing of the patients, no wounds, no daily tasks.' 'Interesting', I would think to myself.

Months into the post, Pat approached me and asked if I would take a walk down to Foster Block where all the elderly mentally ill patients were nursed. He wanted me to collect some gowns to barrier nurse a patient who had shingles. He told me to report to the nursing officer who was expecting me to collect all that was requested and required. When he mentioned this person's name I thought 'Ah yes, I have heard about you'. She was the real matron type and look out if things weren't right. I changed my white coat and put on my suit jacket – a must back then, for any venture outside the ward you had to change and keep within the hospital dress code policy.

Main entrance to St Lawrence's Hospital, Bodmin, until the late 1980s.

Me, commencing a twelve-hour shift at Broadmoor Hospital in 1987.

Broadmoor Hospital's old main gate.

St Lawrence's Hospital staff working at Broadmoor during my time there.

Various press and magazine cuttings covering awards and achievements.

Along with team members, winning and receiving the 2008 NAPICU 'Team of the Year Award' (photo courtesy of NAPICU)

Frank Bruno and myself
(photo by Alan Sterling).

My graduation day at Plymouth University in 2000.

Members of the NAPICU Executive.

In the St Lawrence's Hospital Social Club with Chris Thomas (left), myself and Pat Broderick.

The opening of Bodmin Hospital's Healing Garden
with the Friends of the Hospital and Camilla, Duchess of Cornwall.

As I walked down the long draughty open corridors of the Foster Block, staff and patients were all hurrying about their business. The corridor stretched into the horizon and reminded me of the Yellow Brick Road from the film *The Wizard of Oz*. I remembered feeling nervous. I felt that she would find something wrong in what I was doing or what I would say, being a new member of staff. When I got there, I couldn't believe how nice all the Victorian buildings were, especially Foster Hall, so stunning and bright. I found her office and stood quietly at the doorway, feeling like an intruder. I raised my hand to knock on the door. It felt like a good five minutes before she said, 'Come in.' I entered and there she was sitting behind this huge desk, her wide eyes looking like fox's glacier mints. I stood there completely frozen, like a rabbit in the headlights. She wore glasses that could fold at the nosepiece; numerous nursing badges were pinned above her top pocket. I kept thinking 'your uniform would look better if it was left on the hanger'. She would scowl at any student nurse who would walk around the ward with their nose in the air.

This was a nursing officer who fired from the hip. I introduced myself and stated what I had come to collect; I said how nice the hospital buildings were. A conversation then took place for a good ten minutes as she gathered all the items that I required for this patient. I glanced around the office. (What was that in the corner? A fluffy dog handbag!) I felt that I had made an impression by just being polite, being interested in what she did as a nursing officer, and I was on a winner! In this short space of time I discovered that she found almost everything 'fantastic' and said so at least twelve times, on one occasion three times in one sentence. She could talk for England, and I bet she talked in her sleep. As she raised a pudgy eyebrow and displayed a subtle smile (which could have been aimed at me for pure sympathy), her voice was rising up an octave and from nowhere came this almighty explosion, 'Mr Deacon' she said sternly, 'Are you aware that your trouser flies are down!' I stood there opened mouthed, unable to believe what I had just heard, in fact it could have been lockjaw. I felt I was shrinking into the background and nearly died on the spot; you could have fried an egg on my forehead as I went the same colour as the roses in her vase. I wanted the floor to swallow me up. I quickly turned to the side, zipped up and made a speedy exit, clutching onto the gowns. I walked back to my ward doing a John Cleese as Basil Fawlty strut when I had the chance and when no one was looking, I was so embarrassed, what a fool I kept saying to myself. When I reached the ward I was sweating. I walked through the door and all the staff were rolling around in stitches and I couldn't work out why? Pat steered me by the elbow past the staff and straight into his office. It felt like I had been ordered to the sluice room to clean up my dreadful mistakes. It was the silliest strangest moment I had for a long time.

The nursing officer had phoned Pat informing him of what had happened, and that it should never happen again. 'This is not the way we want to represent our nurses at this hospital', she bellowed down the phone. Of course, Pat was very straight faced feeding this back to me and I remembered him smiling through gritted teeth. I knew that I had to move on from this, you cannot freeze time thank goodness. I spent that evening locked in my bedroom sewing my flies up so that there was no way that they could come down again. Months after that, staff often observed me sprint and dive into the toilet at thirty miles an hour; I couldn't get my flies down! This wasn't helped by the fact that you were far too busy to take time out to use the toilet. If you ran too fast and it wasn't an emergency on the ward, Pat would shout out 'No running on the ward Mr Deacon.' How many times would I hear this said to me? The phrase that was often used was, 'Run only for fire and haemorrhages'. I began to realise that I was walking around twice as fast as I used to, and spent most of each shift on my feet.

Some of the weekends that we were on duty Pat would allow me and my colleague to leave our shift early, knowing that we were young, energetic, and going off out for the night. Pat would come up to us and say 'Have a good night lads.' And in a lower tone looking straight at me would say, 'And no nonsense!' (I'm still not sure to this day what he meant by that!) So here I was with my first real job, with a salary and life was good. I remember getting my first monthly payslip and thinking, 'Bring it on!' Naturally, I found a way to spend it all within a few days.

Every hospital back then had a staff social club. St Lawrence's club was at the entrance of the hospital. This club has so many memories for me about all the good times that were had. Commencing a weekend off duty you were guaranteed an entertaining night on a Friday and Saturday. Live bands, discos and a good catch up with all your colleagues. Nursing staff would put on plays, music quizzes, general knowledge quizzes, bingo, the list goes on. Not forgetting all the Christmas parties in the Foster Hall. I think everyone out there who worked in the hospital could probably think back to some fantastic times had by all. Never a dull moment was had for sure.

1980 and onwards produced some brilliant bands such as The Police, The Undertones, The Specials and Madness. The Kenwyn nursing staff soon caught on to the Police and their hit 'Don't Stand So Close To Me'.

This track had the whole team dancing to the rhythm the way the Police did on their video. 'Roxanne' took us one step higher, and we'd dance in the grounds on our way to the canteen for breakfast. On the other side of the hospital grounds, the domestics and kitchen workers would be coming up the path dancing to the band Madness with, 'One Step Beyond!' They would blow through the saucepan handles standing in for their saxophones.

For so many of the staff on the wards back then, our social time was also spent heading off to the Cornwall Coliseum situated at Carlyon Bay in St Austell. This venue was on the beach and how ideal was this. It staged some of the top bands ever. We would drive down in the afternoon and spend time on the beach, then go to the concert in the evening. I have fond memories of watching Alison Moyet filming the video for her latest hit, 'Is this Love?' Over the years we attended many concerts by Sir Paul McCartney (six in total). The Who, Motor Head, Status Quo, and Thin Lizzy. The list is endless. This venue was on our doorstep – how lucky were we?

A good twenty odd members of staff managed to secure tickets to see The Who play at the Cornwall Coliseum. The band that night really signified something major for all of us present; the electric atmosphere they engendered in us all was unbelievable. They could literally hold an audience in the palm of their hand. Some people were standing there just mesmerised by the stage set up, a jaw dropping reaction. The thundering decibel levels with Pete Townsend jumping up and down hammering his guitar and his arm swinging around like a windmill. The crowd bouncing up and down like waves. The Who were certainly no easy ride that night. I remember watching everyone at the front of the stage looking on with passion. Arms waving, heads rolling, and everyone singing along to the lyrics.

The gig that night was powered by pure energy and excitement. They were raw, couldn't have been ignored. They are one of the loudest bands who delivered the most inspiring music. Days after the concert I remember saying 'pardon' to every question that was asked, I couldn't hear a thing. What was that? The Who used to trash their hotel rooms? Hurl TVs out of their hotel windows? If I had known that beforehand I would never have bought a ticket. (Anyone want to read more about the night The Who played in Cornwall?) Who are you? We don't get fooled again!

These trips to this venue and beach reminded me of the time when I worked on Hayle Ward with patients who were in the recovery phase. The late Roy Blake was my charge nurse at the time. I loved working on his ward. When we held Christmas parties for the patients I would volunteer to do the disco and bring in all my 45 inch vinyl. It also gave you a bit of respite from the busy acute admission wards. One afternoon Roy approached me and two other nursing assistants and asked us to take ten patients to Carlyon Bay for the afternoon. We did a lot of day trips back then to get patients out and about for fresh air and exercise. We made sure all the patients were bathed, fed and dressed in new smart clothes. We would then jump onto the hospital minibus to make our way down to the beach. Patients loved going out and would chat and sing all the way there and back. Once we all arrived in the car park the patients would all want the toilet and a cigarette before making their way to the beach.

What we didn't notice as they all walked in was the sign by the toilets saying 'Wet Paint!' When the patients eventually came out one by one, they had lent up onto the walls where the urinals were and came out plastered with streaks of white emulsion paint all down their new jackets and trousers. I couldn't believe what I saw and remember saying 'No!' Well actually I didn't say it like that! We tried everything to get the paint off their clothes which made it even worst with all the smudges. When we got back to the ward I could hear my knees knocking together as we climbed the stairway and approached the ward door. (Anyone familiar with Keith Moon's drumming?) I was sweating and I could smell it. I was also very nervous, so very hot. I wasn't quite sure what level of nervousness I was at; I certainly had no time to gauge this on a scale of nought to ten.

Roy was a gentle and quietly spoken man and always looked after me; I discovered that if you just did your work you were left alone. He was very patient focused and I always felt that if anyone close to me was admitted to hospital and his ward that they would be looked after, and looked after really well. His face was a picture as they walked through the doorway one by one, he was definitely twitchy and chewing his top lip (by then my knee caps had fallen off). That afternoon he kept calling me 'Picasso' and quietly informed me in his office that I would be doing patient canteen observation duties for the next month! His eyes were bulging out of his face with quiet anger; I had never seen this before. I just stood there staring at him complete and utterly gob smacked. A month's canteen duty? The staff on duty that afternoon kept trying to cheer me up. I appreciated their sincerity and the sympathy that was being expressed my way. I have to say that walking into a paint shop was never the same after that. I knew that I just had to move on and brushed it off.

By this time I had moved into the nurse's hostel situated on the hospital site. About twenty student nurses lived in this building during their six-week rotation, along with fulltime nursing staff. Although nursing assistants didn't usually live here, I had been given special dispensation while I looked for permanent accommodation. As it turned out, I ended up living there for two years. I entered the front entrance carrying my union jack suitcase, along with my matching socks. The lingering smell of over-boiled sprouts made me feel sick. I was going to see and hear some of the strangest things going on whilst accepting them as completely normal. Surely someone was in the background spurring them all on? My first thought was, 'What?' It was normal to witness a saucepan full of water being thrown out of the top floor window as people outside were cranking up their music full blast. Some would run downstairs with their plastic duck ring to get their free shower. Student nurses would surf on their ironing boards straight out of the second-floor windows. The domestics would rock up in your room and start cleaning when you were sleeping. I can remember my door being flung open and my weekly towels and linen dropped on my head. Where was privacy and dignity on this occasion? Our hostel was always noisy with parties going on and the place would be full on with students. No wonder we were all constantly shattered, late shifts followed by parties, followed by early shifts equalled exhausted!

The music scene at this time was Duran Duran, Haircut 100, Culture Club, and New Order. Gary Numan had just started cranking up his synthesiser.

We all had to share the bathroom, toilets, living room and kitchen. I remember cleaning up the kitchen and seeing this mouldy pie. Thinking 'well this is going' I threw it at what I thought was an open window. It wasn't. That was the end of my proud dress code to make an impression. My room was small and square with a narrow bed on one side and a desk and chair on the other, beside the hand basin. It seemed to be colder inside than outside. The living room area had a hit and miss smartness about it. The sinks would over spill with dishes untouched for a good week or more. It was basic, functional, and would be my home for a few years. This being a typical nurses' hostel with endless cups of tea and coffee, or something stronger beverage-wise, provided for all the visitors calling in at irregular hours. And there was always some 4am corridor creeping.

I guess we all realised at the end of the day that our domesticity left something to be desired. The stained magnolia walls echoed the basic interior and the cold feeling. To me this was a bit of independence and I soon settled in. It was great to meet all the new students coming in and having the odd party with them. Well, okay a few parties then. We would all go off and food shop on pay day and we had to make sure that we had sufficient food to last us the whole month. You needed the energy.

A great deal of pasta was cooked come the last week before pay day, and I haven't touched it since! At times the cupboards would be totally bare and you would have thought I had just moved in twenty minutes ago. If stocks were low for me it would mean Monday beans on toast, Tuesday cheese on toast, Wednesday egg on toast, Thursday jam on toast, and Friday butter on toast. The very last day of the month would be mouldy dry toast. Well at least I could cook something, some students couldn't cook a breadcrumb. I also learnt how to make curries and stews. It's beside the point that I never ate any of it. A lot of my cooking didn't behave the way the cookery books said it should. Once we had shopped we would all meet up and pile our plates up with a deal that we certainly would cut back the following week. It never happened. If it meant planning, economising, cutting back on food, or forget about food then so be it, this was now home.

On special occasions, I was known for cooking the odd breakfast on my days off, offering my fellow nurses the odd sausage or a piece of bacon. They never forgot this because most of my cooked food served up was still frozen in the middle. I remember one of the ward sisters had moved in for a month while having some work done on her house. When things were quiet we would both sit and watch the television soap Brookside. I was talking to her one day in the communal kitchen while she was cooking her sirloin steak; we both shared a passion for music. The smell of this steak was just scrummy; I couldn't wait for my pasta, if you know what I mean. I went off to find her a book I had (probably about the Beatles).

Unknown to me she had gone off to get something from her room at more or less the same time, but had returned before me. When I found the book I wanted, I went back into the kitchen and there she was standing in a catatonic position looking gob smacked. I said, 'Oh no what's wrong? You look shocked?' She replied, 'Someone has stolen my steak!' Can you believe that? It was still in the frying pan when I left. I shared my pasta with her (she brought the grated cheese and napkins). Well, it wasn't nice cooking a steak in front of me really was it? But no, honestly, it wasn't me! We never did find out who stole the steak.

Student nurse rotation time soon came around and those of us that were left in the hostels said our farewells to the Truro Treliske student nurses with whom we had shared so much fun and knowledge. They had completed their mental health ward placements and now it was time for them to return to general nursing. Some were re-thinking their careers and having had a taste of what our roles consisted of would want to branch out into mental health. After being such a close-knit group we had all promised to stay in touch as one does. It always happens when things come to an end, you really do mean to keep the friendships going but in reality this rarely happens because everyone goes off into the sunset in their different ways. What I did discover years down the road was you would actually meet up again in years to come, and we did just that. Can you believe this? Some of us met in different countries. These connections amazed me every time, and our paths crossed on several occasions. It wasn't long after that I moved out of the hostel and bought a house in Bodmin. It was time to calm things down a bit.

After working on Kenwyn Ward for one year I felt for the first time in my life that I belonged somewhere. I felt orientated and settled and comfortable. The other nurses seemed to feel the same and we all opened up a bit more, sharing ideas and our walks of life. I felt proud in my uniform even though the stiff collar and starched white coat were uncomfortable. Being part of a team was what made nursing truly enjoyable for me. I never once had that nauseous feeling of entering a ward that some staff have described. The challenge of mental health nursing is that you are constantly encountering new things. Every three months we would rotate onto different wards. We had to view the staff rotation lists that would be placed up on the walls in the Kendall building. I am a great believer in rotation, allowing you to work on different wards, meet different patients and staff. You would learn how different wards operated, their own philosophy. Working with different professionals was a lesson in how to behave and present professionally and courteously. It certainly made me reflect on my past behaviour over the last few years.

I spent twelve years working at St Lawrence's Hospital, which gave me a good foundation in mental health nursing. Of course, there was more to come. Nursing demands a lot from you. I still think it's much more of a vocation than a career. I quickly realised that it would take hard work, grit and sweat to rise through the nursing ranks. I was also aware that I was at the bottom of the pecking order. The charge nurse/sister came first, then the staff nurse, enrolled nurse, third year, second year and first year students. Then us as nursing assistants.

Chapter Ten

Time for Change

I had various friends and contacts in Scotland at the time who were continually asking me to move North to work. I have to say that this was a big decision for me and it took time to think it through. Having mulled it over for a few months I decided to run with the idea. There were parts of me that felt like I was letting my colleagues down. These were the people who had supported me in the hospital and without a doubt made me feel welcome; most importantly they had become my mentors. I had now been working in the hospital for twelve years and we had shared so much together. If you asked me about moving around the country now it would be 'yep' no problem at all and well used to it. I could now sleep on a washing line! (Interestingly enough, you will find that most people have a place that always seems to draw them back to, mine being Cornwall.)

The answer to this move was eventually a definite yes; I felt that it would be a whole new adventure not having lived there before. It would also surely give me a wider spectrum of a different life, including the mental health setting. So I packed up and moved, lock stock and barrel. It wasn't long before I took up a post at the Monklands Hospital in Airdrie, Scotland. This psychiatric unit was attached to a general hospital. The unit had two wards, ward 24 and ward 25 along with a day centre. I moved to Cumbernauld, a town where *Gregory's Girl* was filmed starring Clare Grogan, the lead singer of the band Altered Images. Ward 25 was an acute admission ward and I felt settled within months. The experience I had gained from Kenwyn Ward really gave me that head start.

This was a whole new experience for sure, and I had to get used to the Scottish culture. The accents, Iron Bru, *The Daily Record*, haggis and Radio Clyde. Scotland is Scotland; they have a whole different set of laws including the Mental Health Act. The teams and staff members I worked with were superb; I became good friends with so many of them. They would say to me, 'Noo Pool, dinny think Scotland is nice? Nae wonder you moved here.' I have always had a good ear for accents. The teams I worked with were brilliant and I would tell them so. 'Ach away with you', they would say. They wouldn't hear of any plaudits, especially from me.

They soon caught on to my love and passion for music and were keen to inform me that Scotland had produced some of the finest bands ever, Texas, Deacon Blue, Wet Wet Wet, The Eurhythmics, Simple Minds, Altered Images and The Proclaimers. Sorry, did I forget to mention the Bay City Rollers? Someone must have liked them as on numerous occasions they retained their position at the top of the charts for weeks on end. I had to swiftly get on board with the history of Scottish football and Celtic Rangers. That was my first piece of homework if I was to fit in and survive. Staunch football supporters, through and through. Once I had settled and people observed the way I worked, the same topic came up again and again, 'Why are you not doing your nurse training?' My answer was that I didn't think I was clever enough to sit all those exams, and besides, I don't have the entry qualifications. University? It just wasn't within my reach.

I always felt miserable relaying this to the people I worked with. It was like setting yourself up as a failure before you had even started. It had become a recurrent feedback theme from staff everywhere that I had worked. What it did tell me though, was that I had certainly found my profession or vocation. We had many student nurses seconded to us for placements from Carstairs High Secure Hospital in Scotland for a three-month period. (The hospital later changed its name to The New State Hospital.) I always found student nurses' experiences very interesting and started to get a picture of how a High Secure Hospital like this would operate. I worked in Scotland for two years, and this eventful time whet my appetite for wider horizons and gave me itchy feet to move around.

After much thought I decided that perhaps it would be a good time to return to Cornwall. Cornwall's coastline is truly a spectacular picture with views that take your breath away. Time to slow things down a bit, space to think, walks on the beaches, (at the time I would have stood out like a milk bottle) and get back to a Cornish pasty. The Cornish sea and lapping water, along with the salty smell in the air would always clear your head. I soon wrote to Pat explaining my situation and that after two years in Scotland, I had decided that I would like to return to live and work in Cornwall. I can't remember how I worded the letter but it was basically 'Dear Pat, I need a job, regards'. Pat was straight on the case and it wasn't long before I was heading back down the motorway with a van full of furniture. Months later I was interviewed and back at St Lawrence's Hospital. But things for me felt different.

Chapter Eleven

Change, Evolve and Move On: Broadmoor Hospital 1987–1997

After returning to St Lawrence's Hospital from Scotland and going back to work as a nursing assistant, it felt like everything had fallen back into place. I was back on firm ground, back where it had all started for me. It didn't take me long to get back into the routines of the day to day business of the wards. It was good to meet up with old colleagues who were eager to hear about my experiences working in Scotland. But it was only months down the road when I kept saying to myself, 'Come on Paul is this really it?' I can remember feeling quite trapped. The one thing I really hate is feeling trapped. This isn't meant to sound like 'What *still* a nursing assistant?' So many nursing healthcare assistants are very happy remaining in this position and that is absolutely fine, but I wasn't content with this. One way I summed up my own personal feelings was groundhog day, where every tomorrow is today all over again, and every today is yesterday replayed. By then I had so many years' experience under my belt and felt quite uneasy that I did not have one single qualification.

Someone once said to me that you may have all this experience, but where is that piece of paper to say that you are competent? They were so right. At times I would look at others and think do you know what, I could do that, or gosh you do that well, or would look at others and think you're not really up to that. Again, I started to re-evaluate my future goals and had to decide what to do. It was a frustrating and soul-sapping time. For the first time in my career the fact that I had not trained professionally really started to concern me. At times I would feel quite inadequate. This wasn't 'victim' self-pity stuff, it's all about being self-reliant. For me, this was the best survival strategy, I would strive to compel my circumstances and not be compelled by circumstances.

All the way through my journey I needed a goal to focus on. I realised that it was so easy to get trapped in a vicious circle if you had no idea where you wanted to be because you wouldn't get there. I also learnt that if you didn't have evidence of qualifications you would find yourself employed in a job that you didn't like or career that went nowhere. My thinking back in the early 70s, back at school, was that you had one chance at education, if you didn't fit or achieve then you had blown it. But we should never write ourselves off because at that time we were not academic. There is a second chance around the corner and it was coming. It was very evident to me that if I was going to achieve moving onwards and upwards I had to make things happen myself. It certainly wasn't just going to fall into my lap. The Rolling Stones sang 'You can't always get what you want,' which says it all?

I started my mission and to do this I needed to search out tutors, colleagues and example setters; the people I needed were those that could point the way forward. I must also point out that my frustrations were not displayed in a stroppy manner; most of it was pleasantly internal. This wasn't about blaming anyone, it was just a fact of life. However, at the time it felt like a real blow that I just wasn't getting an opportunity. I can remember quite clearly being on night duty and thinking about some of my colleagues who had left St Lawrence's and gone off to work at Broadmoor Hospital.

I had received numerous phone calls from them over time telling me what it was like to be working within the forensic setting of a High Secure Hospital. I also reflected on the numerous one-to-ones I had had with ex patients who had been detained under the Mental Health Act and were sentenced by the courts to Broadmoor and Ashworth Hospital for some considerable time. They had gone through the system and ended up being placed with us in Cornwall. It was also the time that the National Health Service was going through yet again more radical changes. You will all be aware that from the late 80s onwards, hospitals became much smaller and patients were starting to be cared for in the community by Community Psychiatric Nurses (CPN). As the weeks and months went by I knew deep down that this was my niche and took very little time in writing an application form. Once received, I completed it and sent it off within days. This was such an almighty lift for me. For years I had received so much support and encouragement in trying to get some sort of qualification in order to gain entry to student nurse training. This is what I really wanted to do; in fact I was chomping on the bit.

The second problem was that I still couldn't keep still long enough (Road Runner comes to mind) let alone sit and write an assignment! I had many a conversation with Pat about this move. No doubt Pat didn't really want me to leave again, however he could see both sides of the coin. I respected him for this, as I have previously said, I learnt so much from him. One of the main things for me was to listen to other people, take on board their views based on their understanding. Even if you believe in something and others don't share this, you have to have faith in your own abilities.

I was then informed that, if I wanted to obtain my O levels, the modules would have to be taken all in one sitting; this would give me entry into nurse training. This was not encouraging to me at all. I didn't comment at the time but would roll my eyes at what I regarded as the madness of it all. I didn't feel I had the intellect to move forward with this, it was all too much at one time. I sat discussing various routes with many a tutor back then who also shared my frustrations. However, I had also not taken on board that they did actually teach you in the school of nursing all that you needed to know to become a nurse; you weren't expected to know it all before you had started. I was yet to get my break, it was coming. Sometimes it felt like relentless intensity, at times impossible to sustain. Within weeks I received a letter back inviting me for an interview, it was November 14 1986. If timing is everything then this timing could not have been more right. I was so made up that I had at least been taken into consideration. Unknown to me at the time there were a good twenty ex St Lawrence's staff working at Broadmoor. Some were qualified, others were nursing assistants, and I discovered over time that I knew most of them.

As time got closer for my interview I polished up on my interview skills and tried to pre-empt some of the questions. I selected a few of my colleagues at St Lawrence's to do some mock interviews with me, one of those being Steve Davies who helped me so much. I even remembered to polish my shoes, something I observed my Dad doing when I was younger. On November 22 1986, a day before the interview, I headed up to Crowthorne Berkshire. Driving up the M5 I felt proud and that I had so much to give. This was another break I would need and I knew if I could secure a post, things would change. And boy didn't they! That day became the second step of my journey. This was one of the most momentous things that had happened to me. The hunger for knowledge and self-betterment were on the horizon.

Sometimes I look back and think of all the time I had wasted, but suddenly I was eager to learn all this stuff and it was so interesting; in fact it proved to be life changing. My next mission was to purchase a dictionary (when really I wanted to spend the cash getting my hands on David Bowie's new album). My dictionary became my hub of understanding words. Years later with modern technology, the Kindle and iPad became my modern library.

Arriving in Crowthorne, Berkshire and following the directions given, I drove to the top of the hill to be faced with an 18 foot wall with cameras everywhere. This was 'Broadmoor Hospital' with Victorian buildings and stunning surroundings. It was huge; the wall went around the hospital for miles. Once I had parked the car I met up with my colleagues from St Lawrence's and went off to the social club for a pint with them. We caught up with all the news and immediately I could feel the warmth connecting St Lawrence's and Broadmoor staff; there was a real bond and a wealth of experience on both sides. I had an early night in order to be alert in the morning. My interview was at 10.30 the next day. I was ready suited and booted by 7am. They had put me up in the nurses' hostel and I watched all the staff walking off to start their twelve hour shifts. They were all in a full uniform which I was used to wearing at St Lawrence's Hospital. Although most hospitals were to do away with uniforms later, some twenty years on we are now seeing them return. It has always been said the wheel turns full circle.

I arrived at the old prison-looking main gate reception and was taken to a waiting room to wait and be called. I sat there thinking 'well Paul, here goes; keep it together, stay focused and listen to the questions carefully.' (There wasn't an autocue in front of you with the answers.) I had to remember that so much was common sense. I also kept looking at the 18-foot wall out of the window and the size of Broadmoor. What was it like inside? I remember sitting there feeling a little anxious, finding it impossible to stop my brain from churning through all the ideas and possibilities that might face me in the interview. I waited and tried to forget what I was waiting for.

I was called in on time at 10.30 and taken to the interview room next door and introduced to the panel. I was asked if I would like a drink of water, which I declined. Well, I instantly regretted that decision as my lips were literally stuck together. Or was it the fact that I knew that if I did accept a drink I would miss my mouth and end up dribbling down my shirt? I didn't grab a drink before leaving for the interview thinking that I would be offered one there, and here I was now declining. Oh dear, not a good start. There were three people on the panel, two of them were charge nurses. What I discovered years later was that the panel members' sons and daughters were also working here and were later to become good friends of mine. I kept saying to myself 'Andy Warhol once said everyone will get 15 minutes of fame', I wanted mine today! This was my opportunity to sell myself, today I was the best person for this job and no one else. Looking back, I answered all the questions to the best of my ability. One minute I was excited, the next crippled with nerves.

The panel members appeared to really respect the staff that came to work here from St Lawrence's and later I was informed that management felt that I had received good training, had learnt skills, was polite, worked hard, had discipline, and had the background that they wanted. The panel were taken back that I had included a curriculum vitae with my application as this was unheard of from a nursing assistant at the time. I thought that this might place me in a better position, to make them aware that I was forward thinking. There is nothing wrong with acknowledging your strengths and it's also good when someone else affirms this.

The interview was finally over and I asked loads of questions. I also asked if there was any possibility that I could have a look around Broadmoor before I made my journey back to Cornwall, but the reply was 'no'. I would only see the hospital wards and inside surroundings if I was appointed. I met with all my mates at lunch time who were eager to hear how things had gone. I said that I felt okay with the interview and thought that it had gone well, but you never really knew. I went into the interview full of self-belief. If you are convinced of your worthiness, it's easier to convince others. You cannot be distracted if you know what you are talking about and where you are striving to get to.

The waiting game had now commenced and it could be a fortnight before I would hear anything. Would this be the door that opened for me? This was the opportunity that I so desperately wanted. In fact, it was only six days before a letter dropped through our door. I knew this was it: a brown envelope with 'confidential' written on the left hand corner, stamped Broadmoor Hospital. I ignored it for some time and carried on with other things around the house as if it hadn't arrived. I started working on jobs that I hadn't touched for months, anything to distract me from this brown envelope. The next few hours were both memorable and intriguing.

After plucking up enough courage I opened it and read every word in anticipation. I had been appointed! To say that I was over the moon was an understatement, again I was off leaping all over the house and knew from this moment onwards that things were going to change, they would be different and I felt so elated. My hunger to learn was by now full on. As far as I was concerned the timing could hardly have been better. I can't say that I had one second thought about this move whilst awaiting my starting date. My feet wouldn't touch the ground for a very long time. This was a big deal for me, another milestone. It would be a very different level of nursing to what I had previously experienced. I moved to live in Sandhurst in Camberley, Surrey, thirty miles from London. This was near the Royal Military Academy where all officers in the British Army are trained to take on the responsibilities of leading soldiers.

My Broadmoor mentors were to be John Connelly, Bob Woollams, Chris Hartwell, Mark Watts, Pat McKee, George Tinsley and Tim Brett. When I informed Pat that I was departing and making my way to Broadmoor he was very supportive and gave me words of encouragement that I would take with me on to my next chapter. Pat put his pen to the resignation paperwork and the team gave me a brilliant exit in The Who's 'Keith Moon style' (although my car wasn't driven into the swimming pool!)

Chapter Twelve

Life Just Doesn't Stand Still

Broadmoor Hospital is one of three hospitals in England dealing with psychiatric patients who require treatment within a High Secure environment. This is the hospital's primary and only role. Although associated with prisons and the judicial system Broadmoor is, first and last, a hospital. All the staff employed are nurses rather than prison officers. Although the majority of the patients had been transferred from prisons or directly from the courts, there were numerous patients who were in Broadmoor Hospital because they required treatment under conditions of high security. Sometimes these conditions could not be met anywhere else. One must never presume that a patient has committed a crime, as this is not always the case.

Broadmoor Hospital was designed by Sir Joshua Jebb, who was technical advisor to the government on the construction of prisons. The very first patients to be sentenced to Broadmoor when it opened in 1863 were those transferred from local prisons, asylums, and Bethlem. These were all her Majesty's Pleasure patients found not guilty by reason of insanity. The world's oldest 'lunatic asylum' is in London. The Bethlehem Royal Hospital began admitting patients for treatment in 1403; they were called 'Bedlamites.' Persons that were accused of serious offences who were found to be insane were ordered by the Home Secretary to be removed to Broadmoor, as were those who were identified as being insane while serving long prison sentences. There were five hundred patients detained under the Mental Health Act when I worked at Broadmoor. A new general manager was appointed and he and the new board were looking for change within the hospital.

I worked at Broadmoor Hospital, or shall I say I was also locked up in Broadmoor Hospital, for ten years. Just like the patients we lived, ate and slept there, so it wasn't being much different being nursing staff. Broadmoor was built on a hill in Crowthorne, Berkshire and surrounded by housing estates and countryside. I feel privileged to have the opportunity to reflect on my time working in a High Secure Hospital in the UK and to focus on my Broadmoor experience. I have certainly reflected on each area I have worked in and it's really interesting as I write this introduction, to consider what I will focus on when I come to write about the experiences I had here. Most professional people who walk into Broadmoor for the first time probably have some preconceived ideas as to what it is really like. I would watch people's facial expressions when I escorted them through the gates and onto the wards. Some would ask what it was really like to work here; others remained silent all the way looking pre-occupied.

We were all members of the Prison Officers Association (POA). This was solely because no other union would accept nursing assistants or healthcare assistants at the time. Years later this changed. After my full induction, which lasted for weeks, I was placed on Mendip Ward, Somerset House. Below us was Glastonbury Admission Ward; above us was Taunton Ward which at the time was referred to as the 'lifers'. These were people who had been sentenced to life in prison, and then experienced a mental health breakdown. Once stabilised they would be transferred back to prison. It took time to settle in and balance security and nursing, learning the day to day routines of the wards. I was to rotate round all three wards to get the experience of how each ward operated; this was part of a six month induction for all new starters.

Two characteristics immediately set the forensic nurse apart from other nurses. The first was the role concerning the maintenance of security, and the second was that concerning assessing and caring for the dangerous individual. It was certainly different to my last job. Routines were high on the agenda. I remember many people saying to me that I would get fed up locking doors and carrying keys. This all fell into the role that you were in; we were all here to do a job. A day in the life of the patient and the staff back then started at 7am when the patients were all woken up and once dressed they had to fold their blankets and leave them at the end of their beds. This left them a urine bottle, a pan to empty, which was called 'slopping out'. At 07.10 security razors were handed out and subsequently signed back in. Staff would observe throughout. At 07.45 everyone left the washroom area and had breakfast, again all the cutlery was signed in and out. No one left the dining area until all the cutlery was back in and accounted for. At 08.15 medications were dispensed; patients were called over a speaker system. At 09.00 patients would line up ready to be escorted to their work areas or education. Again, they would be escorted there and back; all staff would radio into the control room so everyone was accounted for. You were also monitored on the CCTV cameras.

At 12pm all the patients would return for lunch, they would then be collected for a 13:30 return to work. 17:00 was tea time, 20:00 medication, and at 20:45 every patient in Broadmoor was locked in their room until 7am the following day. Three members of staff would always be present when a room was required to be opened. So many practices changed over the first three years after my arrival, and I became part of those changes. The introduction of 24 hour care meant that patients were no longer locked in their rooms. Patients had better rooms to sleep in. 'Slop outs' were discontinued and everyone had their own toilet facilities and showers. Balancing care and security were examined. We moved away from prison like work for the patient, focusing on specific therapies. There were new lead posts for staff, better leadership and clearer visions. The environment was improved and there was a better working relationship with prisons. Some staff approved, some didn't and they eventually moved on. I never had one dull day working there.

I don't think that it is an unfair statement to say that High Secure Hospitals have never been popular places. They have rarely had positive plaudits from the public, in respect of all the hard work that went on inside. I can remember some of the stories that were written in the national papers and I was infuriated that they could get away with it. All the hard work done with patients would be totally disregarded; we would be wheeled out on show, into the public domain for further criticism. It has to be said that High Secure Hospitals are different to prisons. They exist to treat patients and not merely just to contain these people. High Secure Hospitals are so different from other psychiatric hospitals, even Regional Secure Units by reason of their security measures.

High Secure Hospitals such as Broadmoor, Rampton and Ashworth (formerly named Park Lane and Moss Side hospitals) have always been open to scrutiny, and still are to this day. This is due to the degree of control over patients confined within the hospital's 18-foot walls, and by their nature they are exempt from many conventional methods of appraisal. They focus on patients who are high profile, who are extremely notorious and very often dangerous. The public continue to ask the question, are we properly safeguarded?

Broadmoor is a very special place; I say this because its existence confirms people's greatest uncertainties of what human beings are really capable of. It has been said over the years that there is no reason to prevent the closure of Broadmoor, that it should be encouraged. I would often hear this said over the ten years that I worked there. Nonetheless, it has also been accepted that in the future there will always be an ongoing need for maximum security. Here now in 2019 we are seeing Broadmoor downsizing. There are no longer any female patients and wards are being closed as I write this book.

In December 2012 work commenced within the existing grounds to prepare for the redevelopment of Broadmoor Hospital. It was a sorrowful day for me to witness the demolition of the old Woodstock, Banbury, Henley and Abingdon wards to make way for the new construction of the hospital. Since 1863 a lot of the old wards had not changed making it difficult for staff to provide the modern services and treatments that patients require.

Patients at Broadmoor require a highly structured and well-staffed therapeutic environment. It is very important that they remain engaged in their treatment to prevent them from becoming withdrawn. Daily treatment programmes are designed to assist their therapeutic recovery. The new hospital will contain 234 beds and it is due to open in 2019.

Large institutions have always been perceived as having a control culture, what with locks, keys, security, cameras, large dormitories, fences, walls, long halls, and corridors with high ceilings. All trademarks of an establishment concerned with the management of large volumes of people. Violence within a ward does happen, and I learnt over time that incidents of aggression could be kept to a minimum if you had really skilled nurses working alongside you. Tensions that might spill over could be nipped in the bud and any patients that would flare up could be dealt with, with the minimum of injury for either patient or nursing staff. Everyone worked as a team and would know what they were doing. Knowing the patient meant that you could pinpoint their triggers and calm and reassure them. What the public must remember is that people admitted to mental health units (hospitals) are frightened, and in some cases terrified. They don't understand what is going on at the time, so it is very important to gain their trust and to build a therapeutic relationship with them. This is paramount.

Whilst I worked at Broadmoor, the hospital undertook a program of change in my first year led by the general manager. It progressed from a history of institutional custodial care to a service that provided therapeutic care. However, there were still violent incidents, patient on patient and patients towards staff. There were serious injuries and there were murders. There were suicides and self-harm was frequent. There is no doubt in my mind that nursing staff employed at Broadmoor are highly qualified – experienced in nursing dangerous people. All staff were trained in what was then called control and restraint; this was a one week course which taught the skills needed to defend yourself, and how to restrain a patient if they became violent. It was certainly good training and designed to restrain in a controlled manner, and at the time it was seen as safe. Later on I went on to do the protective clothing training, where you undertake shield work. This training was intense and had you physically on your knees! I have never had so many lockers and bricks thrown at me. I remember one scenario where one of our instructors role-played a patient who was armed with a knife.

There were nine of us all in our boiler suits, shields, helmets, and our lead co-ordinator spoke to us via a radio that we could hear inside our helmets through speakers. After the countdown we went in to disarm the instructor. I can remember the adrenalin whooshing right through all of us. Once we had completed this procedure we all sat and talked our way through the scenario. When it came to me, I spoke of how well I thought we had all done (day two) 'Really', said Mick Harry who led the instructors. 'So why have you got seven chalk stab wounds on your boiler suit?' Each knife was chalked at the end to show you what could happen and how serious this was. Others then looked at their boiler suits and sure enough a few of us had caught the blade.

The only time the police came to Broadmoor in my days was if the police dogs were requested to sniff out illegal drugs. They were not present if there were potentially dangerous situations; nursing staff would deal with the situation. It also reflects all the special leads you were paid, for example, walking through the gates of Broadmoor every day or night. In years to come, working outside of the Broadmoor walls, I was to learn that there was affinity between nurses and the police. We would often find ourselves thrown together for a variety of reasons. We had similar work patterns, roles and responsibilities; both the police and nurses would at times deal with life and death situations. I learnt a lot from the police over the years. They too had a tough and difficult job to do.

High Secure Hospitals represent the darkest possibilities of the human condition and at the same time the highest ideals of humanity. The balance between security and treatment at Broadmoor were continually questioned as newer treatment regimes were developed, but a percentage of people felt that the principles seemed to remain unchanged. This discussion would carry on for years. Most of the patients in Broadmoor had committed some sort of serious violent offence. Patients admitted to Broadmoor either came from psychiatric services or from aspects of the Criminal Lunatic Asylums as they used to be called.

My own ten-year experience nursing patients at Broadmoor is that every crime that was committed by a mentally ill person there was clearly a double tragedy for the person offended against, and the offender. It was very clear that more often than not, before committing the crime, the offender had been seeking help for some time. Patients would often tell me that they hadn't been listened to when they had requested help, or you would read the build-up to their offence within their notes before they were transferred to us. The role of the various teams was to explore daily the meaning of dangerous behaviour, for the patient that you were working with, the health professional, and the public. There were times when I would be interviewing patients thinking, 'I really need further training here.' You would spend a lot of time communicating, talking to people about their lives, about philosophies and their problems.

I worked very closely with a patient who had killed his wife and two children whilst suffering from a paranoid psychosis. Over the years he did make good recovery; however he was then confronted with the reality of what he had done. This resulted in depression, guilt, hopelessness; it became a daily torture to him. Whilst psychotic he believed that he had protected his family from the devil. He often contemplated suicide, but was also put off as he felt he would be faced by his wife and children who would be asking him questions about why he had done this. As he would recall this harrowing experience, his voice would be flat, devoid of all emotion. He had been forced to repress his emotions for so many years. Some patients are admitted from what clearly appears to be a disease which has resulted in this dangerous behaviour. There were many patients who had committed the very same offence. Suicide attempts and self-harm would be a common feature of life in Broadmoor. This posed a real challenge for those designing the structure, and of course for us as nurses managing them. This dictated a challenge to create a ligature-free environment which reduced the potential to self-harm to a minimum. It's a balance to create a relaxed and patient friendly environment that is not overtly custodial.

Several patients showed a great interest in Individual and group dynamic psychotherapy, cognitive behavioural therapy and social therapies offered along with the creative therapies such as art, music, holistic therapies, occupational therapy and drama. The most amazing experiences I have witnessed are the interactions with patients when they are involved in art therapy and music groups, or working within a one-to-one session. Playing guitars, drums, tambourines or key boards are so helpful in many ways, and a means of communication and self-expression. It relaxed patients to feel grounded. They would get lost in the sounds that they were producing.

Talking to patients over the years, especially those that had formed bands whilst in hospital, I discovered that music helped them to explore their feelings and emotions, and to come to terms with painful memories. Many patients use creativity to try to make sense of a tragic event. They would try to work out a way of exploring what had happened and why. It would be a safe environment to search those unresolved feelings. Patients would do this alone or in groups, and it gave them time to reflect on their feelings of then and now. They would eagerly wait for art therapy groups to take place on the ward, allowing them to use artistic materials such as paints, pens, chalk and clay. These tools would become their expressions. I was so taken aback with some of their paintings, and what they were trying to express.

Inmates at Broadmoor, as they were described by the outside world, are designated as patients rather than prisoners. Whilst many patients are convicted criminals, a number have not committed any crime; their detention for treatment does not stem from an appearance in court. I learnt from working with patients and building a therapeutic relationship over years with some, that locking them away for 'life' to guarantee the safety of the public would in fact just promote complete hopelessness, and you would end up with demoralised staff and patients all round. But some patients have said the most terrifying day for them is the day they get their freedom back. Having been detained for so many years, they had become so familiar with their territory and their safety. People can be seriously mentally unwell and require serious help, but that does not mean prison. If people are a danger to themselves or others then they require that help. People do not choose to be like that, it is totally absurd to think that someone really wants to be mentally unwell. Over the years I have worked with so many people who have had troubled backgrounds. At first it was really hard to understand the difficult circumstances they would find themselves in through no fault of their own. One of the hardest things patients struggle to come to terms with is the loss of purpose in their lives.

Each patient that was admitted had to adjust to the hierarchy of power on the ward, both in terms of pecking order of other patients and indeed of the staffing structure of each ward. The dynamics of this were fascinating if you observed every movement, listened to every word. The patients had to learn who to trust and who were the influential ones. It was paramount for them to know who was dangerous and who was not. Most patients also had anxieties about people they had known before, for example in prisons they had left behind. Their own index offences could be very embarrassing for them; they wanted to be in control of all their information. This was very interesting, as they had been admitted into a system where control was completely removed from them as soon as they walked through the ward door. I noted this over and over again.

All visits to Broadmoor at the time I worked there were held in the main central hall. All visitors were searched beforehand and any items that were brought in were checked and placed in a box which was then locked. When items were sent to the wards they were checked again by the nursing staff. The hospital canteen operated with patients working there under supervision, those that had parole. No money was exchanged but invoices were made out for all transactions. We were all on a weekly rota for doing visits, church attendance or sports field duties. I used to enjoy these as it got you off the unit and mixing with others.

One morning I was on visiting duties, which meant that I would assist in escorting patients to the main central hall; there I would stay for two hours observing the visits along with other staff. Visits would take place between 10am and 12pm, and then from 2pm to 4pm. All patient movement was monitored rigorously from ward to ward. Each time a patient left the ward they were radioed in and out via the control room which looked like an airline cockpit. (I always found this a fascinating place to sit and observe my colleagues hard at work.) On this day, the visiting duty was slightly different and I was taken back when Gary Kemp (from Spandau Ballet) was escorted in to the central hall to meet Ronnie Kray for the first time.

Gary and his brother Martin had formed the band Spandau Ballet in the 80s and have recently reformed, having parted years ago to pursue successful careers in acting. They had many hits in the 80s including their mega summer hit *True*. Gary had requested this meeting with Ronnie to discuss his role in the film *The Krays* in which he was to play Ronnie Kray. The visit lasted about an hour. Gary later wrote in his book *I Know This Much: From Soho to Spandau* that when Ronnie was escorted back to the ward after the visit, the patient that served them came up with the bill – for £100! As they'd only had two shandies Gary queried this and the reply came, 'Hope you don't mind but Ronnie put a few fags on the bill for the interview'! He paid it. It was 26 April 1990 when *The Krays* premiered in London at the Odeon Leicester Square. When the film was released on DVD a core of the patients at Broadmoor watched the film. Reggie and Charlie Kray were regular visitors to Broadmoor.

I met Boxer Frank Bruno on Woodstock Ward back in 1988. This was quite special for me having followed Frank's boxing career over the years. Frank had been involved in High Secure Hospitals for a number of years. He was brought into Broadmoor to assist with the multi gym, a place where selected patients could work out. He seemed so dedicated to what he was doing and I remember, whilst talking to him, how broad he was and thinking of all the fights he had, not forgetting that he was the undisputed heavyweight champion of the world. He was a frequent visitor who was often seen walking around the hospital chatting to staff and patients. Indeed, a great man.

Years later, Frank Bruno went through several episodes of depression and was admitted to hospital. He has written about this in his book *Frank: Fighting Back*, and discussed his side of what happened on *Piers Morgan's Life Stories*. This was a story that he wanted to tell about how mental illness could swat down the strongest man or woman. He wanted people to know what he had been through, and how with help he is recovering. I was teaching twenty odd students the day that the Sun newspaper was forced to retract their callous front page headline about Frank Bruno's breakdown. We discussed this hurtful headline for a good hour; everyone was just appalled. When we returned from our lunch break, we discovered that the Sun had profusely apologised after a public outrage. They also said that they would set up an appeal for a mental health charity. They were clearly embarrassed by the bad publicity and the anger of their readers. Basically, the newspaper was full of inaccurate reporting.

Over the years, there have been many documentaries filmed about Broadmoor Hospital. Our charge nurse took the lead on the LWT *Forty Minutes* documentary of the ward I was working on entitled *Inside Broadmoor*. Our ward and team were the first to move into the new buildings within the hospital and it was decided that this should be given national coverage. The documentary covered various aspects of the hospital and individual wards and how they functioned on a day to day basis. Another documentary followed from London Weekend Television. Nursing staff were asked if they would like to take part. For myself, I had no say, one of the nursing officers said, 'Paul, I supported you when you needed evidence for one of your NVQ projects and you owe me a favour, yes you will take part.' I was filmed in the day area of the ward, carrying out day to day routines with the patients. Documentaries about Broadmoor that were filmed with permission and later viewed before being screened to the public were found to have been edited; they started by showing the barbed wire, cameras, the 18-foot wall, even the sounds of wolves howling. Everything that you could possibly think of that wasn't supposed to be there. Even today, television crews continue to make further documentaries about the hospital.

Chapter Thirteen

All in a Day's Work

One of our charge nurses, who had been around for many years, was very by the book and everything had to be just right. I had a lot of time for him. You knew where you stood and if you did your work then all was fine. One day on the unit there was a feeling that illegal drugs had made their way onto the ward. It was his decision to bring in the sniffer dogs to do a thorough check. All the patients were informed once their rooms had been locked off. It wasn't long before the dogs arrived and once our charge had given them a rundown they proceeded with good results. People would go out of their way to try and bring illegal drugs or alcohol into Broadmoor. We had cocaine packed on the back of postage stamps all ready for the person to lick and stick. We had orange juice cartons brought in with the original contents syringed out, vodka injected in, and the wax seals replaced. (Today things have changed: drones have been delivering illicit drugs to prisons and secure units.)

The charge was pleased with the outcome and the team were brought into the office along with the dog team to be briefed on the outcome. As our charge relayed this information to us, one of the dogs kept jumping up and down and going crazy at one of the staff's lockers. It was enough for one of the officers to say, 'Whose locker is this?' The charge looked and noticed it was his locker. He started turning red and became flustered and started saying, 'The only thing in there is my peanut butter sandwiches.' 'I'm not so sure about that,' the officer said. 'The dog wouldn't be jumping up and down like this, can we have a look please?' By this time, the charge was purple, 'All by the book?' I was thinking.

As he opened the locker the dog jumped up and went in head first and discovered a block of cannabis! We all looked on in horror, I was thinking 'No!' By this time the veins on our charge nurse's neck were standing out like ropes, you could see them pulsating, and I thought any minute now they are going to explode. Mind you, I almost broke a blood vessel trying to stay calm. His teeth kept going up and down like an electronic blind. He was literally bumping his gums. My memory also took a serious kick start when I remembered that he didn't take wind ups on this kind of scale lightly. As I looked at my colleagues in horror they were all winking. 'Oh no' I thought, 'this has been a wind up and he's been stitched up like kippers.' I didn't realise that the officers were in on it as well. 'Right' I thought, 'time to go and went onto the ward ready for the fireworks to go off.'

I walked past our charge nurse who was by then blue and purple. Ten minutes after the officers left the ward he went mad! His voice echoing from the staff room, you could hear the tea cups rattling on the saucers. His voice was hoarse. Was it just a storm in a teacup? It was amazing, after the roar he had everyone's undivided attention! There was no more chit chat for the remainder of the day; he didn't take his eyes off the team until we had all finished our shift.

The prospect of mental illness disorder combined with dangerous behaviour provoked fear within the public mind. This is not helped by sections of the media who often more than not choose to focus on the sensational aspects of incidents that occur. Every day on all the wards in Broadmoor, the daily newspapers would arrive and were vetted before going out to the patients. Staff would also have a flick through to just make sure that there was nothing in the text that would be detrimental to the patients' victim's families. You became very tuned into what you were looking for, likewise when you were monitoring patient phone calls. The press circus was always looking for a story; they would go right out of their way to get one. I learnt a lot about how they operated. I can remember coming off duty many a time and walking down a really quiet road to head home and having reporters approaching me asking for information on certain high profile patients. The reply would always be, 'No comment.'

I can remember one day out in the airing court being on observation duties where patients would get fresh air, play football, run around or just sit and talk. I was in conversation with a colleague when, to our total dismay, we witnessed a thin pole appear over the 18 foot wall with a small camera attached at the end. The press would go out of their way to get a photograph, eager to get some shots of the infamous. Intrusions like these, then spread all over the front cover of the Sunday tabloids all about an individual's private life without consent are totally unacceptable. So many patients were damaged people and had no inner good parenting, no ego, strength, no self-esteem. However, what they did have was their daily immediate pain. We were quick off the mark to notify our security department. We were always referred to by the press as guards, or prison officers. We also had to be alert when we were off duty, in our social time. Members of the press were always out there and we lost a few colleagues who were caught out, which was sad.

Our Perspex high fenced airing court was on the roof top of Woodstock Ward. It was always fascinating to watch and hear Concorde fly over twice a day. Ah, the warm blue summer evenings. The duties out there were awesome and I was well tanned from June until August. People would say to me, 'Paul, where have you been for your holidays? Antigua?' Well as it happens...

One day one of my colleagues formed part of a five person team taking a high profile patient to the Old Bailey in London. If a patient you were working with was due in court you were also assigned to the court case. When you were on an escort to the courts the patient was double handcuffed to two staff members. High profile patients would also warrant police escorts with several police cars. As they approached the court, all the press present ran up to the van which was being escorted by the police. They were jumping up taking photos through the tinted van windows eager to get shots of this person. The court case went on for weeks and weeks.

On one occasion when the papers were vetted, we were all shocked to see a photograph of one of our colleagues in a national newspaper with the words printed below his photo, 'Killer detained and sent to Broadmoor Hospital.' They had taken photographs of the wrong person. You cannot imagine how he felt! He was awarded compensation for this inaccuracy and an apology from the tabloid. Elton John received an apology on the same day from the same paper, but our colleague had a larger column space.

It was true to say that Broadmoor had a far higher media profile than Rampton or Ashworth. Along with close colleagues, I made myself available to spend time at Ashworth to share some of our best practice with their staff. Together, we wrote a comparative article which was published in the magazine newsletters of each hospital.

There were many complaints made to the media from the Broadmoor's board of management, but these were all rejected on the grounds that information about high profile patients was in the domain of public interest. This is what sells papers, all the tabloids depended on sales, and this in turn provided wages. Headlines in the tabloids included: 'Broadmoor cutbacks could set killers free', 'The loonies have taken over the asylum',

'Why was this killer free to roam', 'Di visits Broadmoor? Why?' The day I left Broadmoor I picked up a paper in a service station with the headline 'Broadmoor is not just a hospital with bars, it's a prison, and should be run like one' (*Mail on Sunday*, September 1977). This could be very distressing for the families of those that were detained. In 1995 one of the national papers wrote, 'Truly it is a world gone raving mad when we have to refer to a murderous criminal like Ronnie Kray as a patient.'

Over the years a small minority of staff at Broadmoor would deliberately leak information to the press, in some cases for payment. They were referred to as 'The Moles'. Journalists will read every paper, editors every other editorial, the print will watch the television, and the television will lap up every word in the print. People out there decide for themselves who and what is important. It appeared that the media were always behind the public when it came to knowing what was popular, and what was not. The media is often accused of manipulating events to their own advantage, and to sell newspapers.

Broadmoor is an isolated social institution; the public are frightened by what they see as violence through illness. This has always made Broadmoor newsworthy, and it would attract weekly, if not daily, attention. Scandals were a focal point and resulted in all sorts of distorted articles and distorted photographs. One patient that I nursed who had signed up and given consent to be interviewed for a national documentary, was identified, judged and branded within a three minute interview. He was tempted by the cameras without giving any thought to the longer term effects; the same happened to some of the nursing staff at the time that I worked there. All of them regretted it.

There were two patients who escaped between 1987 and 1997. One from an outside working party who had been authorised parole, and the other whilst on an escort to his work area. He managed to scale the 18 foot wall by climbing the CCTV mast pole which had been installed too close to the wall. Nurses were responsible for the practicalities of the security system. In other countries security staff were a completely separate group from those who delivered therapy. Patrol's searches, escorts, and even restraints on a violent patient may be carried out by separate trained security staff who are employed to do just that.

Every Monday morning at 10am, Broadmoor's siren sounds as a test. The ear splitting wailing from the siren became the soundtrack to my time spent there. This was Introduced in 1952 following an escape, and was the recommendation of an independent inquiry. It can be heard all over Crowthorne, Camberley, Wokingham, Bagshot, Bracknell, and Sandhurst.

One particular day I was on my day off and decided that morning to cut the grass (by this time I was living in Sandhurst), it was a lovely sunny morning and I knew it was going to be a hot one. Half an hour into my task the siren went off. I could hear it clearly over the mower's engine. But it wasn't a Monday and it wasn't 10am! I ran into the house and grabbed the keys to my car to make my fifteen minute drive to Broadmoor. With the nature of the population of Broadmoor patients, the critical incidents were very high priority: escapes from the hospital and suicides. The response of all staff is immediate.

The hospital went into lock down and there would be no movement of patients. Schools were closed, local residents locked their doors, and radio stations put out alerts. Police arrived with their dogs and vans, and everyone had to sign in. Once we were all assembled the security activity was immense. I was signed up to work alongside two police officers and given a bag containing information about the patient, a radio and photos to show members of public when we stopped them at the road blocks. We were assigned to a main road leading into Sandhurst and off we went. It was a really serious matter when someone escaped. Every car, bus and van had to be stopped and searched. The three of us worked really well together and ended up on the shift until 9pm. My lawn mower was still in the garden spinning around aimlessly. The safety cut off switch never did work! The grass was more than cut. I was surprised that no one was playing bowls on the lawn when I returned.

When signalling members of the public to slow down and stop we had to show them our identity badge, the person's photo, explain that a patient had escaped from Broadmoor Hospital and that we needed to search the vehicle which also meant the boot of the car. Most people were fine and were just anxious that someone was out there loose. Others would be really rude and aggressive and would start swearing, having a rant that we didn't do our jobs properly. How on earth could you allow a patient to escape from a Top Secure Hospital. On the other hand, I remember a lovely lady who lived on the street that we were patrolling on, each and every hour, on the hour she would bring us a tray of tea in cups and saucers, never forgetting the chocolate biscuits.

The time that I will never forget was when the two police officers stopped an individual car, leaving me with the hippie flower power van coming towards me. When it stopped, the anxious driver looked really shifty, especially when I asked to get in the back of the van to lift the seats and look inside boxes etc. He kept trying to distract me, so I spent extra time going through everything. There was definitely no-one on board the van so he could move on. He kept saying, 'Oh thank you, thank you.' As he drove off I looked at his tyres and no wonder! They were as smooth as a baby's bottom. He must have thought I was a police officer. We all wore the same coloured vest coats, and I guess this was his connection. The patient was found later that evening, and had not gone far. Others did though.

In the summer of 1996 I was approached by my charge nurse, Pat McKee, regarding a transfer of one of our patients to Jersey. A qualified colleague whom I had worked with at St Lawrence's and myself had been requested to do the transfer to St Saviour's Hospital. My colleague was a really good mate; he loved a laugh and was right into really funny wind ups. I did various escorts like this over the years, and it was really good to do the transfer because I had worked closely with this patient for the last seven years. All the paperwork was faxed to the Home Office who gave us the green light. We were to be escorted to the airport, flown over, then met and escorted from the airport to the hospital once in Jersey. I carried the bag with all the patient information – photos, documentation, section papers and so on – just in case he went AWOL and we had to report the incident to the police. Once we were through the airport security we boarded a waiting escort van, security outriders escorted us to St Saviour's Hospital.

Everything went to plan and by the clock. We arrived at St Saviour's where a two hour handover commenced. Nursing staff made both of us feel very welcome. We said our farewells to the patient and began to walk out towards the entrance. As we said our goodbyes to the staff they asked us if we were staying overnight; we were booked into a hotel and would fly back the next day. We told them our plans and they asked us if we would like to join the ward's evening out. We looked at each other, and with no hesitation said, 'Of course' (like you do).

Jersey is a beautiful island with lovely buildings; there were many places to go in the evenings, and now we would be with a group of thirty odd nurses. When we got back to the hotel we were like two kids jumping up and down and really looking forward to the night, who wouldn't? It was always nice to meet new people (he says, smiling). We shared a huge room with two beds. I pulled the short straw for first go in the shower; we had an hour to get ready. I've already mentioned my colleague's sense of humour, and I had been on the receiving end of some of his previous hilarious wind-ups. Off he went into the shower as I made coffee and turned on the 14 inch television to listen to the local news. I sat on the bed and unpacked all my gear – checking that I had packed my best aftershave – and started to go through the bag of confidential information I had brought with me, along with photos, paperwork, and phone numbers.

I looked at the 14 inch photo of the patient that we had just transferred and a plan automatically fell in place. Sitting there I thought, 'Yes, this is going to be a cracker.' I took the photo and stuck it around the rim of the TV screen and spent time making sure that it looked reasonably professional. I sat back on the bed and thought 'wow, watch this!' This will pay him back for all the things he has put me through over the years. I sat there bursting and couldn't wait until he came out of the shower, it seemed like hours and hours, 'Come on' I kept saying to myself, 'Hurry up and get out of the shower.'

Eventually the door opened. The bathroom was quite a distance away from the television. 'Look our patient has absconded from the hospital', I shouted out loud. His face was an absolute picture as he looked up, 'What!' He said, with a look of total horror. 'No' he kept saying as his whole working career raced by in front of him. I don't have the exact words to describe the look of fear that swept over his face. Within those seconds of looking at the television screen and seeing the patient's picture, he failed to hear the commentator in the back ground covering the Jersey weekly farming news!

Moments later the penny dropped and relief flooded over him! We were both rolling around the floor with laughter. It really was a picture. This pay back stunt went around Broadmoor within 24 hours of our return, and boy did he get ribbed. We had a fantastic night in Jersey with the staff from St Saviour's Hospital, who were superb. We arrived at the airport by taxi the following day at 10am for our flight back; there was thick fog all the way. Once through the airport entrance we were informed that due to the fog all flights were cancelled. So another day and night in Jersey was had. We managed to visit the underground hospital. It was just as the Germans had left it in 1945, with wards, officer's quarters and fully equipped operating theatres. Fascinating.

Chapter Fourteen

Positive Times

Diana, Princess of Wales, visited Broadmoor on two occasions, and I was privileged to meet her. She arrived at Broadmoor Hospital on 14 November 1995, as the patron of the British mental health charity Turning Point. On this day she opened the therapy unit, and a centre for research into psychiatric disorders linked with violence.

On arrival she was escorted to Woodstock Ward. It was unusual for a royal to make a visit to Broadmoor, but the Princess of Wales helped those who were sick and dying, visiting not only Stoke Mandeville and Great Ormond Street Hospital for Children, but a High Security Hospital as well. It was a very exciting day as she was by then the People's Princess. Outside the wall there were a lot of people dashing about. Police were on duty and extra security was everywhere. Once they heard about her visit, the public started to gather outside Broadmoor's reception area. The press were also present, along with television crews covering the visit. All patients on the ward were screened before the visit, and there were some that didn't wish to meet her, or couldn't for security reasons. Security was always tight at Broadmoor, but this day was even tighter. It was planned that Princess Diana should get involved and talk to patients as she had requested. Prior to her visit she had expressed an interest in attending a patient's multi-disciplinary meeting, obviously with the patient's consent.

Her security staff were everywhere on the ward, I made four of them a tray of tea in our staff room (and made sure that I swished the teapot with hot water first!) It was fascinating listening to the messages on their radios and the rundown of Diana's journey towards us. She eventually arrived on the ward where we were all lined up to receive her, and was greeted by our charge nurse (who was grateful that the police dogs weren't brought in). She shook hands with medical directors and the chair of the board. She was absolutely stunning when she made her entrance.

Since her separation in December 1992 she had been judged on a daily basis by a jury of either the press or the public. So it was nice to see her looking relaxed, friendly and interested in what we did. She was taken on a tour of the ward, and met and chatted to selected patients who gave her a rundown of their day to day schedule within Broadmoor. In total she was on Woodstock Ward for a good hour before departing to her next scheduled ward visit. On one occasion one of her minders suggested to her that it was time to move on, but she insisted on further time. Throughout the hospital visit, there was no further patient movement until she departed. There have been many high peaks in my career, and this was definitely one of them, an extra special moment.

There were times at Broadmoor when things became quite stressful. Some days there were incidents after incidents. There were many that I was personally involved in, and two in particular wake me up at 3am in a cold sweat to this day. I keep thinking that if it didn't go the way it did, what would be the consequences now? Some patients had nothing to lose and were either in Broadmoor or prison for a very long time. Everyone's fear was of being taken hostage. A memory of the seclusion room door being closed on me and the patient still in seclusion even now leaves me and others feeling cold. There has never been an explanation as to how this could ever have happened. My colleague thought I had exited the room. I was swiftly removed in seconds but it seemed like minutes.

We were a close bonded team on Woodstock ward, as well as a very forward-thinking; some people regarded the ward as flying the hospital flag. The team had many forms of support for any staff member after a serious incident, including one-to-one or group supervision. An incident that is still discussed in Cornwall today, started as a colleague and I were standing outside the laundry room and trying to keep everything calm. It was mentioned that there was no way that I could climb inside the industrial tumble dryer that was used daily by the patients. This was all a bit of banter, but I did remind my esteemed colleagues that I was the smallest member of the team, and of course I could fit inside. I was also aware as I sized up the round entrance to the dryer that I was the person on the security radio, in charge of all patient movement, and all the emergencies. I remember throwing out a bet first for a bit of fun, and it wasn't long before the readies appeared, crisp blue and brown notes. Without any hesitation, and some patients getting involved with this banter, I started to climb inside the tumble dryer and eventually secured myself. What was I thinking of?

What I didn't expect next was for the tumble dryer door to be closed and the switch to be turned on! As I looked out in disbelief, by now treading the warm wheel like a hamster, my radio called an emergency for staff to attend an incident on another ward. Can you imagine my facial expressions trying to relay this message to the team whilst spinning around? My lips stuck to the glass rim door and I was searching for my lip balm. All I could taste was washing powder and I started chewing fluff. I really felt like I had spent an entire hour spinning round and round, stewing with the heat, munching on sesame seeds. I also learnt that hamsters feel potholes, bounce over speed ramps, and use the odd bit of bad language. The grinning-disgruntled hamster in a uniform. However, in the end it did all work out as my unusual facial expressions were eventually interpreted and staff members were dispersed to the other ward. The remaining patients on the ward looked on with laughter, but it really broke the ice and the ward became more settled. Here in 2019 I tend to look at our family hamsters (Charley, Millie Moo and Spike) in a different light to other people, when I see them spinning round and round in their cage wheels. This story still goes round today; it seems to get mentioned at Broadmoor and here in Cornwall amongst NHS staff. I wonder how that story got around?

It was a quiet day on Woodstock Ward. I was doing the security checks with an hour left on my shift. Security checks were paramount and checked by two staff and signed for on each occasion. Staff were playing cards and snooker with patients. Most of the patients had been out to their work areas that day, and the evening was their time out. My charge nurse came over to say that we were expecting a celebrity visit, the person was on site and had requested a visit to our ward. To be honest, at the time we didn't really know who this was. One of my colleagues did say to me, 'Hey Paul, it might be McCartney!' Yeah, right!

It turned out to be Jo Brand the comedian. It wasn't until I asked and discovered that she was a comedian and had in the past worked in mental health as a ward manager. She entered the ward with escorts and our charge nurse took her around so that patients could speak to her. She came over and spoke to us about our roles and how long we had worked here. It was all very informal and she came across as very caring. Since this visit and watching her on various television programmes, including *Never Mind the Buzzcocks* as a guest, I have found her very funny. I wished I had known more about her before she arrived.

Over the years I have taken student nurses and work colleagues from Cornwall up to Broadmoor for the day. This provided an educational day, giving them an insight into how the Broadmoor system worked. It was a real eye opener for them, some having nursed people who have stepped down and progressed from a High Secure Hospital to a Regional, and then to a Medium Secure Unit. I would point out that as this was their first visit to Broadmoor, their impressions may be based on media and popular perceptions of the hospital and the patients. I suggested that they observed all the hard work and dedication that went on and spoke to the staff and patients before making their own judgments. They had a good deal with these visits, as I knew so many people there, and we always had a good day. Nursing staff would escort them around the wards; I would catch up with everyone and reminisce. Yes, the tumble dryer story would surface yet again! And the Christmas staff dinner incident which I will get to.

Broadmoor and St Lawrence's staff were very close. People looking in would be touched by the way colleagues from both hospitals would rally around when the chips were down. You cannot buy this generosity, you cannot buy this friendship. True friends are very few and far between. When I say friends, I mean people that have earned the title over many years. These people were givers rather than takers. Teresa 'Treza' Hartley and I had started out as nursing assistants at St Lawrence's around the same time in the 70s. Although I didn't know Treza that well whilst working at St Lawrence's, our paths crossed many times in our vocational routes, and social gatherings. Treza began working at Broadmoor a year before me. We would often meet up and reminisce about the past. One day on our breaks, we continued a discussion that we had started months earlier about organising a big reunion with the staff of St Lawrence's and Broadmoor.

Our vision transpired into a mega reality reunion, and one I will never forget! Aided by Tina Parker, Gary Brandon, Steve Temple and Steve Davies, we arranged for the event to be held in the social club at St Lawrence's. We certainly all felt passionate about what we were doing. I contacted the local newspapers and radio stations to advertise it. I was sure that it would be brilliant publicity and wanted to highlight that the event was being organised by mental health nurses. All this publicity was drumming up attention locally and nationally. Word had spread. From day one we wanted to aim high; we were on a mission.

The event got coverage in the papers and on radio stations from Edinburgh and Glasgow to London, Birmingham, Bristol, Manchester and Leeds. We drew up lists and lists of people to contact, slowly working our way down them. Word of mouth also began to spread and soon people began to contact us. We wanted to capture all those that had moved on. Knowing that this event was waiting on the wings, I was contacted by Radio Cornwall and did an interview for them at 6am from my bedroom on the morning of the event. Little did I know that it was going to be plugged on the hour, every hour in their news bulletins. Our colleagues managed to hear it on their way down to Cornwall. We made banners, hung balloons, laid out food, sent out flyers and hired the best DJ going, blasting the venue with lasers, pyrotechnics, a good bag of sounds, including one Beatle song! We also had our photographer on board. It really is the best memory I have of Treza and I actually sitting down and pulling off something so brilliant out of nothing. We spent hours changing things around, getting the evening to fit.

Press cover:

The reunion at St Lawrence's Hospital

An evening of St Lawrence's Hospital Past and Present is to be held on September 8th 2001. More than 400 people from across the country who once worked at the Hospital in Bodmin are to meet up at the St Lawrence's Hospital Social Club to catch up on old times and watch videos of the past, along with a firework display. One of the organisers Staff Nurse Paul Deacon said, 'This is one of the biggest reunions that we have ever organised, but it wasn't easy and has only been made possible by the hard work of all those that have organised it. Because previous nursing staff have moved all over Britain, we have had to be quite extensive with our publicity.' As well as emails, flyers, letters, banners, and faxes, we have made announcements up and down the country on local radio stations. The evening which includes a live band and disco, will also include a showing of old videos and photographs. Staff who have left St Lawrence's Hospital and worked at Broadmoor Hospital will also be attending the evening.

We erected a huge screen at the back of the stage to play several hours of old St Lawrence's footage, a bit of history. The entire venue was properly set up with bars, lighting, sound system and back drops, we even had a marquee set up outside. One of our colleagues who had left St Lawrence's had gone on to manage a unit in Bristol; he also became the medical advisor for the BBC series *Casualty*. I had replaced him on Kenwyn Ward as a nursing assistant; he went off to commence his nurse training. He managed to bring loads of different items to the evening that had been signed by the actors in the series – even a plaster cast! We raffled all of these items and the money went to a mental health charity.

With less than an hour to go before the scheduled start, all six of us organising the event were shattered before we had even started, and we had ploughed so many hours into this event. In one area there seemed to be a chaotic scene taking place suggesting that any hope of starting on time had been abandoned. There was a lot of fussing and loud voices with very little evidence of any headway being made. Apparently fireworks were now off the schedule, but someone had managed to get some large bangers. Above all the shouting that went on I heard, 'Well take the fag out of your mouth first before unwrapping them.'

The evening was a phenomenal success with ripples of electricity. So many people attended that it was packed solid. You could feel the passion that everyone shared in the enthusiastic mingling and chatting. The sweat was running down the walls and the atmosphere and the ambiance around the place was incredible; there was a constant buzz of excitement. It was as if someone had sprayed fairy dust all over the venue. Staff entering the venue were greeted with the thunderous handclap stomp of Queen's 'We Will Rock You'. Shaun Dawson, a close friend of mine who had only worked at Broadmoor, soon became good friends with all the St Lawrence's staff. This was good for him as he had heard all about St Lawrence's over the years.

It took me back to when four of us (all nursing) were called the 'Spacers' because we used to hold music disco evenings in the original St Lawrence's social club. They were really wacky evenings that brought the crowds in. All of these events raised money for charities including Mencap. A lot of laughs were had and memories recalled – we even had a twenty-minute video of the Spacers shot around the hospital grounds. The hospital management at the time supported all of us in these events, and there were a few. They were also seen as events which raised the profile of all the creative, positive, forward thinking staff who were working as nurses and cared so much for their patients. It was great to feel that we were at least doing something to help.

Chapter Fifteen

National Vocational Qualifications at Broadmoor Hospital

I wasn't sleepwalking into my first qualification, it was reality. I am adamant that through my second chance of education I developed personally and academically. I'm always keen on the idea of self-improvement. Setting clear goals for my vision became a must. It was very hard at first but believe me it soon became challenging and fun in a most positive way. I felt reassured and justified that what I had set out to do had been the right approach. Academic studies felt right. I thought this was an interesting and positive move, but some people looked at me in a bewildered manner and questioned my thought process.

Since starting my employment at Broadmoor Hospital, I really had gained so much experience in a range of different clinical settings. I made a real effort to work on most of the wards to gain experience as they were very different. During my employment as a nursing assistant, healthcare assistant and finally lead healthcare assistant, I endeavoured to make the most of opportunities made available to me and grabbed any opportunity that I saw coming my way. But the question still hung over me 'Why are you not training to be a nurse?'. The answer was simple, without any O levels, I couldn't even apply to start. But then an opportunity arose: the NVQ. By grasping what was offered with both hands (and a lot of hard graft) I eventually achieved a number of qualifications and certificates which enabled me to further develop both individually and professionally, and led me to start my student nurse training in mental health. I gained an NVQ level two (NVQ2) and level three (NVQ3) in Developmental Care, an A1 Assessor Award, an Counselling Certificate and a Healthcare Assistant Drug Assessment.

Through these various courses I learnt so much and was very fortunate to work alongside professionals who encouraged and supported me to develop these skills, and to expand my contribution to the daily delivery of care within the team of Woodstock Ward. Some of these senior professionals had written many books including the late Dr Murray Cox (psychologist). I had a lot of respect for this man, and I am forever grateful that he invited me to participate in his anger management groups. This of course supported various units within my NVQ course and I covered the group therapy unit modules in no time. I was then able to put all this theoretical knowledge into practice under the guidance of the qualified staff.

The courses that I attended really boosted my self-confidence, without a doubt it gave me more insight into understanding all the patient illnesses and their treatment plans. My whole outlook on what I was doing within my role was changing day by day. My knowledge was growing and I found everything interesting. I felt passionately that I was making a difference for the patients on a day to day basis. It's a combination of common sense, hands on experience and study that produces success. Theory complements your practice. Getting yourself started is often the most difficult part in any process.

At the end of 1994, I discovered that nursing assistants could now enrol for an NVQ2 in Developmental Care, which was now being offered in all four High Secure Hospitals in the UK. I started to delve deeper and asked to speak to Mick Pither, the co-ordinator of the NVQ programme about this new vocational award, this was truly an opportunity that I had been looking for. All of a sudden, I had a great moment of clarity. Within weeks I was signed up and wasted no time in attending the NVQ study days. I was now registered as a candidate. As I signed up, I couldn't help but think back to the previous year and all my hours of hush–hush studying in the library. I had kept going back to read up on mental health nursing, and knew that I felt drawn to it. I wanted to make a difference in the profession and help people who needed care and compassion. Some people are uncomfortable around illness, but I wasn't.

I can remember walking home with my pink NVQ folder under my arm thinking that, after all those years working in mental health, I now had a qualification to aim and work towards. Remarkably, even at this earliest stage of the NVQ, I was acutely aware that this award was going to be special to me. NVQs highlight the different routes to gaining professional qualifications. They are work related qualifications and are designed to allow you to learn in a way that suits you. They give you the skills that employers are looking for. An NVQ3 is equivalent to an A level. To achieve this , I had to prove that I had the ability (and competence) to carry out my job to the required standard. I had to work towards an award that reflected my role in a paid or voluntary position. The A1 Assessor Award enabled me to assess NVQ candidates. You had to be occupationally competent, occupationally qualified, and actively working in the care sector.

The reality was that it was a happy time for me. As you can imagine I was impressed. A personal and satisfying feeling, it was about developing and moving forward. Taking steps towards learning the process. Everything one could ever want to get started was right there in front of me. It was all now beginning to fall into place and I was getting on board. I had been given a green light and a direct route to this award. I was going to grasp this chance with both hands. It was all do-able. This message would be hammered home to me, time and time again.

Once I had harnessed the NVQ format I wanted to learn more and more about my chosen career. If it's something you're doing because you want to progress to a higher level, then you need to use it as an opportunity to demonstrate your skills as an ideal employee. This will enable you to gain the experience and confidence to move onto whatever it is you really want to do. My Developmental Care award fitted into my then ward base, a 25-bed personality disorder unit (Woodstock Ward). With guidance from the NVQ co-ordinator and the five ward-based assessors, I was off like someone participating in an egg and spoon race. You have to give credit where credit is certainly due. Without the ability of great assessors acting as my mentors I would have gone nowhere. All of them are genuine people – a total bonus. My mentors would always go that extra mile, in fact the extra 99 miles. I had surrounded myself with people who could help and support me, helping me to put any minor setback into perspective. This was one of the many times in my career that I felt that I was working with the cream of the crop.

All of the ward staff were made aware of all the NVQ units I was trying to achieve. I made a list of all twelve unit headings, which were stuck up on the office wall. This helped everyone in the handover and sign-posted assessors to what I was doing that day, what could be covered with observations and witness testimony statements. I learnt very quickly that you needed to be proactive and do your homework first. It was no good going into a supervision session and fumbling around, as this would irritate people and demonstrated from the very start that you were not at all organised. Later I would learn all about time management and load prioritising.

I completed the NVQ2 award in less than a year, working flat out. I was immensely proud of that achievement. I ate, drank, spoke and slept the NVQ. On reflection I can remember that it was such a pleasurable feeling moving onto level three and having some background knowledge of the process which made it a lot easier. I remember attending all the relevant study days at Broadmoor's Education and Training Department, the workshops, seminars, conferences in order to gain all the underpinning knowledge that I required. I have to say that I was in my element and flying with it all. Without any doubt, this very first award reinforced my belief that if you believe in yourself you can do anything. I had all this excessive energy at my finger tips and was raring to go. Back then NVQs were big on paperwork for evidence, and nothing like today. I remember the external verifiers coming to see myself and the co-ordinator. 'Right Mr Deacon, we would like to see all your evidence for units one to twelve.' I would literally wheel all my twenty full folders in on a fork lift truck! I'd become a little nervous under the scrutiny of the examiner and colleagues would say, 'Don't get in a fluster Paul, we'll tell them what a terrible nursing assistant you are!'

After all the hard work, the hours, concentration, assignments, presentations, exams, study, the cherry on the cake was about to arrive. Once I had completed the NVQ3 I began to realise that I was in fact capable. I knew deep down that I could make a success of it. I had the feeling of taking control of my career pathway and everything seemed to be working out smoothly. I was promoted to healthcare assistant and was re-graded. Months later I was appointed to lead healthcare assistant with a lot more responsibility for the implementation of new initiatives.

There is no point whatsoever in having good ideas unless you can implement them. I would know when I had a good idea because it would stay with me. It would come to me in the early hours of the morning and I'd get it down on paper. If it was still fresh in my mind when I woke up in the morning, I'd discuss with the team and if agreed, we'd look at implementing it. As the months rolled by, I'd find myself thinking more and more about what we'd just implemented and whether it would work. Before you had time to think, another whole project had sprouted wings and suddenly taken off.

At the time this was seen as a brilliant career move and I found the role a real challenge. The lead healthcare assistant posts at Broadmoor were the first of their kind. There were times where I was thrown into the deep end and sent to important meetings. Management would be sitting around the table talking about things I had no understanding of. It was easy to lose an opportunity to gain from this experience because I'd be so uptight about getting it right, but I didn't understand this at the beginning. All this chomping on the bit was now becoming a reality. I was now allowed to dispense medication under the supervision of a first level nurse, orientate new nursing assistants to the ward, co-facilitate ward based groups such as anger management, self- awareness, life skills, social skills, assess and support NVQ candidates, document and contribute input to care planning, the list went on and on. I really felt that I was being supported by the whole team and found that if I showed an interest in learning then people would bend over backwards to help.

It was always good to keep your sense of humour as well as it was a lot of hard work. I am a great believer in making things enjoyable, it helps you to survive. Even the patients would say, 'Hey Paul perhaps this would help with your NVQ', if I was doing something with them that day. By this time, I felt I was a real team player. It was always inspiring to have students nurses on the ward for their three-month placements. This would always lift the spirits of the team as it brought in new ideas straight from the universities. The same went for medical students. What made it work so well within this team was the fact that we were all so different, yet each of us had a great deal of experience in our own area of nursing. We all got on well. The chemistry really worked. Any issues were dealt with in a proactive way. I would sit quietly and listen, then when I had my turn I would make sure that what I was saying was valuable and relevant to what was being discussed. I would tell myself to think rationally and sensibly. You don't have to be loud or forceful, just communicate in a clear and concise way.

It was also good to approach your peers with solutions rather than problems. Continuous supervision on a four-weekly basis with my mentors was welcome. There are certain people you really want on your team when the going got tough. People who were approachable, grounded, straightforward, and knew what to do in certain situations. They can be your greatest asset, loaded with common sense. We were all often reminded that the team would be incomplete without us individually. In my supervision sessions I was told that I was here because I was good at my job, that I had been chosen through the interview panel because of this attribute.

The combination of good planning and passionate staff is exactly what you need to have in a successful team. It's all part of the skills that makes a ward team stand out from others. Every three months, staff rotated to other wards, and some found these changes with staff quite traumatic. However, there is a lot of sense in rotation. A fixation on retaining people when you were essentially trying to change things doesn't always work. They simply represent history while you and others are busy building and implementing the future. What motivates one person in the team may not motivate another. Change can be good.

Back then, NVQs were the most offered choice for providing evidence of learning that could be scrutinised and accepted by prospective employers, and they remain a vital part of training. Who would have thought that in years down the road I would become the NVQ co-ordinator in mental health for Cornwall? It could be argued that before NVQs were set up, many workers like myself would not receive any recognition at all for their skills.

One evening, whilst on duty, I was monitoring a patient's telephone call (in line with Broadmoor security). I happened to notice an English National Board (ENB) training handbook. Whilst looking through this booklet I noticed that certain universities accepted the NVQ3 in Developmental Care as an entry qualification for student nurse training. At the time I remember feeling very excited. I telephoned the ENB to have this information confirmed. I spent the following weeks tidying up my portfolio and arranging for references.

This was to be a massive breakthrough. In the mid-nineties, a very important statement was issued from the UK Central Council (UKCC) – now replaced by the Nursing and Midwifery Council (NMC) – stating that an NVQ3 in care was an acceptable entry qualification for pre-registration nurse training. They recognised that many healthcare assistants had practical hands on care experience, were familiar with the care culture and often had experience of working within a 24 hour / seven days a week environment. Both the Department of Health (DH) and the UKCC advocated education for healthcare assistants, and recommended fast track nurse training.

My mentors and ward manager were really on the ball with their references for me; I was blown away with what they wrote. Even management came on board and I ended up with references from the ward manager, charge nurse, unit general manager, director of patient care services, consultants, unit nurse advisor, consultant psychologist, and the speech and language therapist. I only required two. Not being able to decide which ones to forward, I sent them all! It also sent a warm message to me that they had faith in me. Weeks later the application forms arrived and I spent hours completing them. Within months I had a confirmed interview date.

Along with all other prospective candidates, my interview was held at the University of Exeter in Devon. Dressed in a suit and polished shoes, off I went feeling proud that I had even come this far on my journey. The interview day consisted of participating in group work, writing a short assignment on a given topic, and then the interview. The tutor who interviewed me appeared impressed with my portfolio, and the standard of training that the education department at Broadmoor Hospital was delivering. I felt really good about the whole experience. A few weeks later I received confirmation from the University of Plymouth, I had been accepted for my student nurse training there. University wasn't about finding yourself, it was about creating yourself. Back at Broadmoor news was flying around the wards that I had been accepted, people were really pleased. I guess looking back there was also a bit of unconscious pioneering for the NVQs, 'Hey look: it can be done, especially in the High Secure Hospitals.'

Professionally, in January 1996 the year began positively. Most of us need at least eight hours sleep a night, I was working on four. I slept with my eyes open and hadn't blinked for three weeks. You just had to be 'bothered' to make the effort to achieve. Although there wasn't much time for sleep, the motivation and drive that each unit module demanded abolished any thought of sitting down with a cuppa and a read of my monthly music magazine. At times it would be difficult to regulate back into a normal sleeping pattern. There were many nights when, exhausted from work, I would gladly have slept on the floor where I had been studying. It was really hard work and I required the utmost concentration. Day and night just merged into one, and weeks mashed together like a hazy blur. They say that our brain is more active in sleep than when we are awake. Memories are a bit like a computer memory stick where information is captured and stored. Mine may have deleted some of the content.

I was invited to attend a presentation at Broadmoor Hospital for gaining my NVQ3 award, along with my Counselling certificate. This event was the first of its kind; it was even more special as it was focused on healthcare assistants. A lot of management attended along with the general manager who presented the awards and certificates. I can remember feeling very proud of myself, that I had achieved these qualifications and that all this hard work had been recognised. It was paying off. It took me back to the gates of St Lawrence's Hospital and the reasons why I had come into this profession in the first place.

There wasn't a day that went by when I didn't think about all the tuition I had received from my mentors at St Lawrence's Hospital. I would keep them updated on my career pathway. This wasn't about all the help they had given me and by the way thank you and goodbye, it was just the opposite. There was no doubt at all that over the years I had been managed by people who were superb at leading teams on a busy ward. It was connecting with like-minded people who would support you on your journey, as they had been supported on theirs.

In Broadmoor's internal magazine (Broadly Speaking) that month it read, 'Exam Passes Make Hospital Proud', and went onto say that I was one of the first candidates in all four High Secure Hospitals in Britain to complete an NVQ3. To my surprise, I was mentioned in the *Nursing Times* and the *Care Standard* journals. It also mentioned that the NVQ3 in Developmental Care had gained me a position at South West Clinical Schools, part of University of Plymouth. I received many letters of congratulations including those from the general manager, forensic consultants and colleagues from around the hospital.

It was not long before I commenced the D32/33 NVQ Assessor Award, and the Healthcare Assistant Drug Assessment course, which would both take me one year to complete. It was also interesting that some of my work colleagues who had originally had a bit of fun at my expense about the fact that I was doing all this training, now came along to this event to support me and began to seek information about how they could enrol on the vocational training too. They shook my hand, congratulating my success. I would later assess them for their own awards, and later still mentor others. Years later, these candidates were then in a position to apply for their nurse training, and are now all qualified registered mental health nurses. Doesn't that make me feel proud? I have always channelled a lot of energy into people to help them find strength and stay positive within their work area. It was paramount that they should stay focused even when they got tired, weary of the same routines, procedures, the same conversations, and the same buildings.

On 6th March 1997, I received the certificates for my assessor awards at another Broadmoor presentation. It was obvious from the onset that this was going to be more than a fleeting shake of the hand, nod of the head, then back to the ward to work. Not content with one award, I was shortly to receive another. I was blown away when I also received an award for outstanding achievements along with several nursing books for my nurse training. I was totally speechless. It was such a proud moment – probably the proudest moment I have had. Months later I was nominated for a national training award by Broadmoor Hospital's Training and Education Department – my second. There was certainly a whiff of achievement in the air that day. I knew now that things were changing and that I was on the road to further learning. I felt the hunger to get there. I was becoming more aware and informed, better read about the profession I was working in.

Everything about the event was so different to anything I had experienced, yet at the same time had some bizarre sense of familiarity. Had I been dreaming of this for such a long time? I was staggered that they could have that kind of faith in me, but they did. Within this level of competence there was still, I think, by and large a sense that I had something to offer. At times I felt that I needed someone to take hold of my wheel so they could steer and leave me on automatic pilot, because it was full on. But so was my determination. When you are spinning on a merry-go-round, it can at times be hard to see what is going on all around you, making you almost dizzy. Had you any idea how much hard work was going to be involved? How exhausting it all was? Have you any idea what a joy it also was? I would arrive home after my shift, and the only track I could think of playing at the time was Queen's, 'Under Pressure'. Although Black Sabbath's 'Changes' got a few spins too!

Off-duty people would be having conversations with me and my eyes would roll back in my head from tiredness, but it was a manic kind of awake. Working and studying twelve hours a day for how many days? On my first day off in weeks, I was like a slug. There isn't a book that I have ever read that says that you sleep with one eye open after you have travelled this far in education. Everything happened so quickly. Looking back, could all of this have taken place in just over one year? It did, and I called this period of my life the 'Road Runner Year'.

I think of all of the years that went by when I had dismissed myself, saying 'I can't do this', fuelled by the fact that I couldn't sit still for five minutes. Then I received even more positive news. Broadmoor Hospital had found funds to support a number of healthcare assistants to go off and do their nurse training. When I heard this from my manager my mouth nearly hit the floor. Mick our NVQ co-coordinator, had a massive smile on his face when he told me. I was so overwhelmed and couldn't wait to start. I went around the ward with a constant smile saying 'yes!' to myself. It felt too good to be true. Honestly, the good times are amazing, but the little bits in between can at times be, dare I say it, tedious!

Four months later, I was called into the ward office to discover that the promised funds had fallen through and it would be another year or so before money would be available. They say life gives with one hand and takes away with the other. So I decided to move back to Cornwall anyway and commute to Plymouth. Other healthcare assistants did take this opportunity the following year. How would I cope at university sitting behind a desk? I am a firm believer that determination, initiative, motivation is just as important as the university you manage to get into. You must not rest on your laurels, times change and you need to move with these changes. It's positive to be looking for something else and you shouldn't just stay in one area of practice. I had built a good rapport with the nursing colleagues around me, those with years of experience, leadership skills, enthusiasm and charisma. Any self-doubt had melted away into the background. As ever, it goes without saying that some of my leaders went the extra mile, despite all the obstacles that faced them on daily basis.

The time had now come to depart from Broadmoor, and what a stomach wrenching time this was. I'd spent ten years working within the walls, getting to know most of the staff and patients, and after all the support they had given me it just seemed so unbearable. We'd spent so many happy, sad and joyful years together and now my time was up. I had so many friends and we had been through so much together. Everywhere I looked inside of Broadmoor there was a story to tell, now it was time to say my goodbyes. Working here was a huge stepping stone in my career, taking me onto a new path towards opportunities that I would not regret. I had had to work really hard to get this far, it wasn't easy but if you believe in what you're doing then you can succeed. I like to see the positive outcomes and learn from what happens to me.

It had been a wonderful experience and very rewarding, but it was now time to move on. Behind the scenes my colleagues were planning a farewell bash; in fact I ended up with three. They planned a pub tour in Wokingham, a party on a boat trickling down the River Thames, and a joint St Lawrence's Hospital – Broadmoor Hospital bash in the staff social club in Cornwall. All three were fantastic and will always remain with me. During the evening I was presented with cards, a cake and the Beatles Anthology video box set. I was over the moon. I wonder how they knew I liked the Beatles.

I then commenced planning a trip to Vancouver. This would give me the opportunity to spend quality time with my family, away from my career and familiar things. I was pleased about the whole idea of three weeks away from study, the humdrum routine of everyday life. Having been on the go for so long, this would be fun. Life had been very intense and serious what with all the studying, it was time to enjoy myself. We all have completely different ways of switching off, of becoming totally detached from work when we want to be.

On the 31st August 1997, after the boat trip leaving party down the River Thames, we arrived back in Crowthorne in the early hours of the morning. I was still trying to digest the fact that I was really leaving the next day, how kind everyone had been, how supportive they all were. I would certainly miss this lot. We had all shared our glitches, concerns, hopes and aspirations for the future. It was as If we were all at crossroads.

Standing with a lump in my throat, I said my farewells to all of them. I was now about to spread my wings. Looking back, the build-up to leaving was a very emotional time. At what point did the realisation finally kick in? The moment when everything crystallises, and you know it's finally over. In my case I have to admit it was a good few years. My outstanding memory of it all was that it was an incredibly happy time in my working life. The fact was, everyone took their work seriously but we also had a good time. I truly am lucky enough to have experienced this sort of 'sensation' for the thirty odd years of my nursing career.

With all my packed boxes and suitcases lined up by the doorway, I looked around with more than a tinge of sadness. Who would have thought that in years to come, I would be back in a different role! In the early hours of the morning a few of us sat around having our last beer. I will never know to this day what made us turn on the television so early in the morning; we would normally be listening to music. It was really bizarre because every television station was showing coverage of Princess Diana; she had been involved in a car accident in Paris and was seriously injured. Hours later the Princess, who I had been privileged enough to meet on more than one occasion, died.

Chapter Sixteen

The Social Side

It wasn't all about work at Broadmoor; we had so much fun as well in our social lives. What was really good about Berkshire is that you could get on a train and be in London in 40 minutes. A core of us had 'on tap' access to all the top bands that were on tour, playing either at Wembley, Earls Court, the Docklands Arena, and not forgetting Reading Festival. It was nothing to see three or four top bands every couple of months playing the circuit, including (among many others) The Rolling Stones, The Who, Paul Weller, Aerosmith and Queen (five times).

I love London. To me it represents escapism and I welcome that buzz. Sometimes I would dream of living through the 60s when this was the place to be, 'Swinging London' packed with busy commuters all rushing around, all going in different directions. If I was in London working, attending conferences or training, I would get up early and spend time watching all the hundreds of people getting down to their business. Bus drivers, taxi drivers, café owners, newsagents, people up at all hours doing what they do. The pace of the traffic passing through, the typical retail British high street, tapas bar, McDonald's, sandwich bars, theatres, markets, restaurants, florist shops, iron gates, banks, gift shops, KFC, kebab shops, and so on. Wherever I went, there would always be something or somebody that intrigued me, someone on the train station platform, a poster, someone sitting in a café. What was their life? Parents? Famous? Rich? Occupation? Hey, was that Ringo Starr just jumping on a double decker bus! I would also see random people with no schedules, no purpose in life.

Even today one of my all-time favourite tracks is Ralph McTell's 'Streets of London'. My closest mates and members of the Deacon family moved to London because it was their vision to be in the fast lane. It was where things were at, it has always been the centre of a fantastic city, a dream where everything happens. On a daily basis people move into the city of

London with new ideas, in music, fashion, art, and then people will move out with even newer ideas. How healthy is that? Another bonus with London is going to local venues and soaking up the electric sounds. There is always an air of excitement about a clutch of up and coming talented guitar bands waiting to make the big time.

There were many Broadmoor staff family celebrations, weddings, christenings, birthdays, engagements, wedding anniversaries, reunions and BBQs. Sadly a few divorces and funerals too. On some occasions we would all meet up for tea 'in the garden, Dahling', with the posh china of course. Treza would look most important as she sipped her tea from a bone china cup and saucer. As she picked up her cup, she always managed to have two fingers in the air! We would listen to, Radio Head, the Crash Test Dummies and REM. Nirvana would be blasting 100 decibels across Crowthorne. There would be plates of fresh creamed cakes, sticky jam doughnuts, sandwiches, sausage rolls, cheese, biscuits, and Swiss rolls. On one memorable occasion, friends caught my facial expressions anxiously looking at each plate. 'What no window cake?' I asked. From the next table someone shouted, 'For goodness sake Paul, grow up. The next thing you will be asking for is red curtains made out of icing on your silly window cake.' I took umbrage at this comment, and later, when no one was looking, I took my shoe off and whacked his swiss roll ten times! It went everywhere.

I remember one summer's afternoon when friends had invited me to the Annual Henley Royal Regatta, along with a grand picnic basket. Berkshire is very picturesque, and the scenery is stunning. Many of us used to enjoy driving to Henley or Windsor, spending time by the river whiling away the afternoon. It was great to spend time as a group of friends and connect with the softer side, in contrast to our full week of scheduled duties. It was like a form of meditation for us all. It allowed us to shut out the pressures of the Broadmoor world for the day, and we'd trickle back home when the time was right.

On the way to Henley on this particular day, I mentioned that George Harrison had a mansion in Henley called Friar Park (Liam Gallagher of Oasis lived close by) and that the band the Traveling Wilburys (of which Harrison was a member) often made appearances in Harrison's specially built recording studio. 'Oh yes,' they said, 'we can drive you there and you can have a look at the entrance lodge and the surroundings.'

Well this just made my day. When we arrived I was straight out of the car taking photo after photo, just as George Harrison himself would not want me to be doing as he had become a recluse to a certain degree and just wanted privacy. He had recorded so many of his solo albums here including his mega triple album *All Things Must Pass* which made number one in Britain and America. There were signs on the high walls requesting privacy. Fans had spray painted Beatles' lyrics on the walls, and George's solo lyrics, including 'My Sweet Lord'. I had the same buzzy feeling inside of me that I'd had when I visited Abbey Road Studios in London, and the famous zebra crossing from the Beatles' album cover.

George Harrison had always worried about being attacked by a stalker or a disturbed ex-Beatle fan, especially after the tragic murder of John Lennon. His worst fears were confirmed on the 30th December 1999, when he was attacked in his own home by an intruder. The attacker, who was from Liverpool, believed he was possessed by Harrison and was on a mission from God to kill him. He was acquitted of attempted murder on the grounds of insanity and detained and sent for treatment at Ashworth High Secure Hospital, Broadmoor's sister hospital in Liverpool. On the 29th November 2001 George Harrison died of throat cancer.

One of my colleagues, who also worked on the same ward, was fully aware that I loved music. He was great friends with a well-known band from the 60s and 70s and frequently met up in the pub that he went to in Berkshire. The band was called The Marmalade and had had many a hit in the 60s, including a number one with a cover of the Beatles' track *Ob-La-Di Ob-La-Da* from *The White Album*. He asked me if I wanted to come along and meet them one night, so I took up the offer and spent time asking questions about their successful career. David 'Diddy' Hamilton was also present, a well-known Radio Two DJ in the 70s (a favourite back then with my Mum). The Marmalade signed a disc and band photograph of theirs for me which was a double bubble for the evening. This was another one of those great evenings which I will always cherish.

The entire Woodstock Ward team were invited to a wedding reception. A popular and close colleague of ours was about to get married to a nurse who also worked at Broadmoor. They were well suited for each other. They always did things in a grand style and the wedding and reception lived up to this. We all got into cars with our dapper black and grey suits, white shirts and bow ties, and departed in a convoy. We were off to a lovely swanky hotel in Wokingham, some twenty minutes away from Crowthorne. There was a feeling of a real bond between the thirty-odd of us in the team. We all worked hard, and today was a day for celebrations and chill out. Most of us were social butterflies, floating from one function to another. The drivers knew where to go and it didn't take long to get there. We poured the tepid dregs of our Costa coffees out of the car windows as we pulled into the venue car park. We were surrounded by BMWs, Porsches and double-barrelled names. I'm thinking, 'Right, okay'. Personalised registration numbers and postcodes seem to be important to some people. As we entered this beautiful and glamorous venue we were greeted by waiters and waitresses who offered us all a glass of champagne. Our charge nurse was leaping around checking our egos before we entered! Well, we are off duty I thought to myself.

The scene was set; we were there with little sign of frazzled nerves or hysteria. There were various groups of people who didn't know each other, but that didn't stop people dancing, mingling, laughing and having a drink. The day can never be repeated. After twenty minutes of settling, mingling and observing (as nurses do) I happened to start talking to a gentleman who was standing on his own. I said, 'Wow what a venue, look at all the flowers.' He mentioned that he hadn't seen the married couple yet, and we placed bets that the bride who I called Mandy would look stunning. He looked at me strangely, paused, and said, 'Mandy? Mandy who? It's Tania.' and he pointed, saying, 'There she is over there talking to Carol.' This wasn't Mandy; we were only at the wrong reception! Throwing back his head he laughed, and I half laughed as I responded, 'You've got to be joking!'

I was feeling good that day. It's my goal to be as comfortable as possible, especially when you were out socialising. But now I had to gather the team, who were chatting in groups, to tell them that we needed to leave at once. Their faces were confused. It was one of those precious moments when I wished I had my camera with me. The gentleman was in fits, and said, 'Oh well at least you all had a free glass of champagne.' Our reception was somewhere else on the same site.

We all bundled out apologising profusely and found our way to where we should have been in the first place. Despite this fabulous day of celebration, it felt that some things were against us. We had done the rounds of thirty-odd requests for what everyone wanted to drink, and two of us made our way to the bar. Eventually we were done, the money was handed over and the two of us carried our trays with fifteen drinks each back to the tables. I got halfway across the bar area dodging everyone dancing when the wooden tray snapped in half! 'Nice Day for a White Wedding?' No, Billy Idol didn't turn up to sing! I wished he had.

My colleague and friend Dave Brazendale was a real card, who brought many smiles and laughter to many of the staff when it got tough at work. He always enjoyed a wild reputation and had a kind of stage presence. He could walk on the ward, stand still and look not saying a word and we would just all fall about laughing, not at him but with him. Sometimes you would think someone must have done something that we couldn't see, but it was just him. He would get a laugh when I never would have believed there was a laugh to be had. Patients really approved of his humour. He wanted life to be big and loud, and should have gone down the comedian road. Dave had a data bank of jokes bagged for every shift. We had so many laughs that at times I can remember having tears rolling down my face.

This is what was needed though, how else could you get through some of the not so good times. I worked alongside Dave for many years and was best man at his wedding. We are still in contact to this day and met recently to clarify events, looking through his archive of photos that had been taken over the years. It was nothing for him to ring the hospital porters and ask them to remove his colleagues' lockers and take them to reception with a sign on each locker stating 'To be collected and stored'. Staff coming on duty would see their locker in the reception area, and their faces! Nine times out of ten they knew who was behind this.

It was a frequent event if we were all out having a meal in a restaurant. We were always the noisy table. Dave would inform the waitress that it was his birthday and we would just look at him in total disbelief. Minutes later the waitresses would come over and sing happy birthday to him while all of us looked away cringing, he would just wink and sit there lapping it all up. Surely they would soon click on as none of us would be singing (this was the tenth birthday celebration in one year and we had heard this line in many restaurants). One night he got a free bottle of wine and a birthday cake with candles (we all sang on that occasion). When the time finally came and it was his birthday, the waitress would say, 'Yeah right.' Dave phoned me recently and six seconds into the conversation he informed me it was his birthday. I hung up! Ker-ching!

I remember one blue sky day we were off travelling up to London to see Michael Jackson at Wembley Stadium, London. He was doing his *Dangerous* world tour. Dave and I were at Victoria station and it was so busy. Having lived in Cornwall for a number of years and doing everything 'Dreckly' I said to Dave, 'You need to stick with me because I don't want to end up lost, or on the wrong train.' 'No worries' he said. As the train approached the station I said 'Is this the one?' 'Yes' he replied, so I got on. I couldn't believe it when I looked out the window and saw Dave hanging out the window of the train on the opposite side and departing shouting, 'See you at the gig!'

The train compartment was in an uproar, with passengers witnessing the fiasco. They were very good though, and sent me in the right direction. Thanks Dave! The Michael Jackson concert was on a Sunday, and we had several hours to burn when we (finally) arrived in London. Back then pubs weren't open on a Sunday until the evening. Dave said, 'Okay, let's go and get a pizza and we can get a beer to go with it.' Two and a half hours later, and plenty to talk about we went to pay and the lady said, 'And how was the beer for you sir?!' (No mention of the meal!) The bill came to £45. Dearest pizza we had ever had, and we shared it. Dave would never do the overpriced meal anyway.

We also had several trips to France, mainly a core of us from Woodstock Ward. Most wards would organise trips out, or have five a side football games playing against other wards.

One day Dave ordered some flowers for his partner for Valentine's Day, because he had forgotten. He asked for them to be delivered to the main reception at Broadmoor, and requested that they should put them in a bag as he didn't really want the world to see him walking out with this bouquet. Well, they arrived okay. An announcement came over everyone's ward radio that Mr Brazendale's flowers were ready to be collected when he left duty. His face was one of horror! He certainly got a ribbing on the way out, as we all had to queue up after our shift until all the wards were secure and taken over by the night staff.

Undoubtedly the funniest and most memorable moment was one Christmas day and on duty on Woodstock Ward. A member of staff in the team said that he would cook us all our Christmas dinner as long as we would do his duties. How nice of him, so we did. Dave laid the table and it was looking grand. We had several sittings as staff needed to be out on the ward. If you were ever to let go of your cutlery whilst eating or take your eye off your half-filled plate, our charge nurse Pat McKee would always whip it off the table and it would go straight into the washing bowl. Pat was a stickler for this. You just knew he was behind you, tea towel over his shoulder ready to pounce. Thinking about Pat's ferocious tidiness, I wonder if that's where I get it from.

Every half an hour one of us would pop our heads around the door to see if our chef for the day was alright. He was sweating like mad with the heat, and the turkey smelt so nice. When we sat down with our grand chef having plated up the last dinner, he caught his legs around the table cloth and dragged his whole Christmas dinner into his lap! It was one of those moments where you needed to be there. All of us were in stitches including him. Well he did have six foot legs! We recycled his Christmas dinner – i.e. picked up the meat and vegetables off the floor and carried on as normal. Dave was still on the floor uncontrollable, and the trouble is laughter is so contagious. If I could freeze frame this moment of time! They say laughter is the best medicine.

I remember being at an evening dinner with friends of friends, there were about twenty of us. I always enjoyed this as there were people that you didn't know. I have always found it a real challenge to walk into a venue of two hundred people knowing only five of them, or if I need to speak to an audience. The subject at this particular dinner got onto what everyone's occupation was and it went around the table one by one. We had a builder, a car salesman, a banker, a brick layer, an insurance broker, a general nurse, a shop manager and so on. It was then my turn, 'I work at Broadmoor Hospital.' Well their faces! When people discovered where I was working, their mouths would hang open in awe. Nine times out of ten they would say, 'I don't know how you do it.' Eyebrows were definitely raised. And that was the start of a two hour conversation; they all seemed so fascinated, interested, or was it mystified?

I've never really been overly concerned if people know what I do for a living when I first meet them. However, the next time this happened it was, 'Who me? Oh, I work for the water board.' There were times when you would be sitting next to or facing a person who would struggle to make conversation. We have all tried somewhere in our lives to have conversations with someone who just sits and does very little to contribute, or are they just bored? Either that or they haven't quite finished defrosting.

Over the years so many people have asked me, 'Did I hear that you worked at Broadmoor? Is that right you worked at Broadmoor? Oh, I didn't realise that you worked at Broadmoor.' When I explored their questions, so many have said, 'Well we just couldn't imagine you working there.' My question back to them was always, 'Well what kind of person did you think worked there?' You always knew that it would be the stereotype full on rugby player come bouncer image in some people's heads. Working at Broadmoor is all about the skills that you had learnt and used in practice. You were trained to listen and if a nurse really listens, then the patient would feel safe to open up. If they are listened to without criticism or judgement their confidence and self-esteem will grow. When you are patient with yourself you can be patient with others.

I have to say that looking around at what others do for a living doesn't always inspire me. The idea that I am actually going into a psychiatric ward every day to help people who are at their maximum crisis point is something I love doing. To be able to make a difference in people's everyday lives. If everyone is supported to feel good about helping those less fortunate, then in the long run everyone will benefit. A lot of positive things can come out of bad experiences. I do feel that there is a lot of dark stuff in this big world. After all, we do live in an age of confusion and cultural upheaval. If you can shine a light in the darkness then it will help to make it a lot brighter for people.

Chapter Seventeen

Everything Changes with Progress

There were a minority of people back home who still thought, 'What Paul, the working class boy from the streets of nowhere had secured a place at a university to train as a nurse?' I Left Broadmoor Hospital on 31st August 1997 to commence my student nurse training at the University of Plymouth. I wasn't nervous, I was far too positive for that. I viewed this move as a launch pad for my nursing career. On my first day of this three year course I cannot tell you how different I felt, back in a classroom setting with desks and chairs, with my pencil case and an apple (I would sneak the odd Mars bar in). This would become an backdrop to the next ten years of my career as I enrolled for module after module. I loved learning and was now surrounded by so many tuned-in people. We would all be together for lectures on anatomy and physiology, psychology and sociology. My favourite lectures and seminars were the heated political ones. The first year comes back as if it was yesterday, as I re-entered a world of discipline and routine. Initially, we were educated in the terminology of nursing.

This was a far cry from my schooldays, surrounded by people with different mind sets and different backgrounds. How did it differ? I wanted to be there, I was mature, and this would be my second chance. I was happy to sit through the first year of the basics (despite having twenty years' experience). Not once did I feel it to be demeaning. You also knew that you would be competing with young eighteen-year-olds just out of school. I listened intently to every word spoken by the tutors and put one hundred percent effort into learning. I really did everything within my power to get things just right. Things were moving fast and results had to be delivered.

After spending the first ten weeks studying within the university campus, I found myself working on my first placement on an acute admission ward at St Lawrence's Hospital. This was very different to Broadmoor, especially when a patient approached me and said, 'Paul, I am just off out for an hour?' Obviously my thoughts were 'How? There's an 18 foot wall!' The tutors would often draw on my experience in the classroom setting.

Assignments and exams were tough and not a sail in the wind. Most evenings were spent writing assignments and I can still feel my eyes moving up and down, up and down, reading and checking each reference and each quote. It took me very little time to settle down into academic life and I loved it. At first the thought of those exams was a bit daunting, but it didn't take long to get used to them. I can't say 'exams again' because there was never a time up until now. When they did arrive, I had never been more prepared for anything in my educational career. To this day I can still remember most of my results.

My first experience of giving someone an injection was something I will never forget. I was trying my very best to remain calm and go through the motions as if I had done it so many times before. Overseen by the ward sister, who tapped her fingers on the cupboards, drawing up the injection left me shaking. I placed the plastic syringe, alcohol swab and cotton wool ball into the tray and took them to the patient's room. I checked the patient's name against the prescription sheet to confirm that the right person was getting the right medication. Taking a deep breath, I drew a cross on his right buttock, as I knew I had to give the injection in the right upper quadrant of the muscle to avoid the sciatic nerve. After three deep breaths I gave the injection. 'Thank you nurse,' he said as he got up off the bed. 'I can tell you have done this many times before.' I felt so proud as I scurried back into the clinical room that I miscalculated the door entrance and bounced off the frame! From that day on I never had a problem giving injections. How lucky was that?

The posh, educated voices of the tutors always commanded a little more attention and respect. Throughout my training I would quite often sit quietly and reflect on the fact that working through the NVQ framework certainly assisted me to adjust to this three year course. At times, attending classroom modules seemed a little bit like being back at school. Here I would go again being the joker of the cohort, but I was always very clear about getting the work done. I knew when to curtail humour, and leave it to others who were younger.

There was one tutor who was coming up for retirement with just over a year to work. This tutor could talk all four legs, ears and hooves off an aging donkey. Many a time I would offer the tutor one of my gobstoppers, and one day I offered the entire bag! The subject being delivered that afternoon wasn't the most inspiring (which wasn't always the case). However, on this occasion, I could see that the cohort were becoming restless and starting to drift off, looking out of the window, yawning and doodling. Others were slipping into a coma of disinterest. I was fumbling around in my bag under the desk looking for my Mars bar. The tutor had put us into groups of five to discuss the pros and cons of whatever the topic was at the time.

The tutor was called out of the classroom for something and was gone for a good twenty minutes. Of course the groups diverted and started talking about their weekend plans, who they were seeing, putting on make-up and doing their nails. I sat chomping on my Mars bar, nibble, nibble, munch, munch. (I was forever getting dark looks whilst trying to extract sweets from their wrappers whilst the tutor delivered a session.) I must admit, I was the only one in the class who could peel an orange in their pocket. I learnt not to open the sweet slowly because the noise went on for ever. It's no different to when you enter the house late at night and try creeping around with squeaky floorboards or opening creaky doors. It just has to be done quickly otherwise it just creates havoc.

When the tutor returned each group had to feed back to the whole cohort. Oh dear, I thought this is going to be interesting. There is always going to be one group that will remain focused throughout the entire three years training, and sure enough that group went up to present. This gave everyone extra time to at least get something written down on their flip chart paper. Halfway through their feedback the tutor looked up in horror, 'Oh good gracious me' she said, 'look at the time, I had no idea that it was so late it's nearly twenty past five. I am so sorry, please pack away your books and we will continue tomorrow.' Everyone looked at their watches, and I noticed them grinning. I had no idea that one of the students had wound the clock forward by nearly two hours! And off we went to the beach! I was a bit annoyed to be honest, because if I had known this was going to happen I would have packed my bucket and spade, and taken enough money with me to buy an ice cream with a flake.

The next day was not good at all and you could hear the sweat dripping off people's palms entering the class, the person who had changed the clock was having difficulty with his breathing, I was on stand by and thought I better not eat this second Mars bar just in case I have to resuscitate. Thunder was just around the corner. 'Please take your seats' I heard (I just felt like standing due to my agitation). 'Right, own up! Who changed the clock yesterday? Come on who was it? No one leaves here this afternoon until I find out who is responsible. Come on don't shilly-shally about.' She was seething (so was I inwardly). For some reason her eyes were fixed on guess who? Yes me. I was often pulled to one side for not paying attention because of my tendency to do two things at once.

The look on my face must have been pretty familiar to my younger educational days. 'Oh dear' I thought, 'Surely not the cane at forty years old.' Can't you see that I am the mature student here? (Or had she been privy to read my past secondary school reports?) I was desperate not to inflame the situation. I tried to speak but nothing came out despite clearing my throat twice. If I could speak I had no idea what I would have said. I nearly broke out laughing and yet at the same time I could feel the hairs lifting on the back of my neck. Anyway, under peer pressure, the person did come forward and was informed that he would be staying on after the lecture; the rest of us could go. It was really funny, and *time* to move on. When I saw him days later I asked him how he had made the time fly? 'I threw the clock out the window.' Was the reply.

One of my most inspiring times as a student nurse was during my second year and working in the community. My mentor was so proactive. At the time you could choose your mentors and I feel that I did this well throughout my three years training, because I chose the ones who were the most dedicated, those that really wanted to teach you all their learnt skills, and wanted you to succeed. At this time I met Chris Thomas who was an art therapist in the community; he was, and still is, so creative with his art skills, and had a brilliant rapport with the patients that he worked with. With Chris as my mentor, we decided to set up an afternoon group for all our young patients. We looked into hiring a hall for every Tuesday afternoon and discussed what we needed to have in place to move this forward.

We then discussed with each patient what we had set up for them and their thoughts on this. It was really interesting that all seven patients signed up to attend. The group was very informal and the sessions would involve painting, playing guitars, walks on the beach, meals out to socialise, cooking, and all the things that would interest them. What was so positive was the fact that the group ran for a good twenty-odd months. It was such an opportunity for these people who in fact lived not far from each other to discuss their mental health problems. This would be on a one-to-one basis or in a group, they were not alone and this helped to reassure them. Comforting skills play such an important role in group work.

Facilitating ease and relaxation with group members promotes trust, openness and honesty. It was sad when the time came to leave the group after four months due to my new placement. After discussion with my mentor and my next ward-based charge nurse, it was felt that continuity played a huge part in this group and I was released from my next ward placement every Tuesday to co-facilitate the group for another four months. My thinking at the time was that this group facilitated patients to do little things that would make their lives more bearable.

Now I had the 'Golden Key' that had opened the doors for me to gain access to university. For all those who doubted it, it can be done. The experience that I had gained as a nursing assistant and healthcare assistant over the years certainly helped me to assess various issues that came up within my training, both practically and theoretically. I have very good memories of my training, and enjoyed every minute of it; to me it was a real achievement. My tutor back then was and still is a superb tutor, another person I have great respect for. He didn't want students to pussyfoot around him but to challenge him. This is when your training kicked in; it gave you confidence to do so. It most certainly polarised an opinion. There was nothing lukewarm about our opinions or debates, you would either love or hate them. Opinions are the cheapest commodities in this world. Just because everybody has one, it really doesn't mean that you have to accept it.

Again, I became heavily involved in all the other roles that were connected to being a student nurse. How did we learn? Well this was the best of university life where you learnt on the job and from the second and third year students, who in turn learnt on the job from those above them. I did feel that you also required the enthusiasm, passion, will, tirelessness, the hunger and the need to do it and complete the three year programme. My training, with exams and assignments surprised me to a certain degree, despite needing extra tuition I got through them all with good results. For myself, any assignment percentage improvement highlighted the power of determination. As I've said before, the main thing about further education is that you only get people attending because they really want to be there.

Here are a few words of advice that I offer from my experience as a student nurse on my first placement:

- A week or so before you are due to start your placement, arrange to go into the ward and introduce yourself. Make sure you are clear about your shifts and what is expected of you in the first few weeks. Ask if there is anything you need to read up on. These questions need to be asked, even if you think they sound silly (they don't).

- You can read about procedures until there coming out of your ears, but once you are working with people with mental health problems, you will discover that things don't always go as planned.

- Don't depend only on your allocated mentor. There are other people within the multi-disciplinary team who also enjoy teaching students. This may include doctors, occupational therapists, psychologists and experienced healthcare assistants.

- It's natural to make errors on your placement. Don't take them hard. Try to turn them around and learn from them.

- The first year is all about basic nursing care. The key is remembering your limitations, you will have to be seen as competent so don't undertake anything that you have not been taught. Lots of students will feed back to the cohort about all the wonderful tasks they have carried out. What is not mentioned is how to make a bed, undertake observations, how to communicate with a person, or how to fill out a fluid chart. All these are basic skills, but are paramount in this role.

- Keep a notepad in your pocket for reflection, this really helped me throughout my training. It also helped me compile my portfolio. Use flashcards for revising.

- Some things will seem tedious but try and get something out of them.

- If a patient asks you a question that you don't understand, ask a qualified member of staff to answer them. If you stay around you will be able to listen to the answer and learn from it.

- Always make sure that you know what you are doing. If you have been asked to carry out a task for the first time, make sure you are properly supervised.

- I have spent many a shift making trays of tea. You may think that this isn't a student nurse's job. But it enabled me to have conversations with all levels of nursing and medical staff who would end up explaining procedures and policies to me. I received a fantastic learning experience from these people with the aid of a teabag! It's also a good way of bonding with other professionals, including third year students.

- Be professional at all times. I know at times this can be challenging. Sound off in a room off the ward, or in your car if something is getting to you.

- There is nothing wrong with having confidence. However, having said that, there is a thin line between having a bucketful of confidence and arrogance.

- Remember to accept feedback and criticism, and remember that it's not personal. It will help you to grow in the role.

- If you have some time where you aren't doing anything on the ward, have a look through the cupboards in the clinical room and tidy up. I learnt that by doing this I knew exactly where everything was kept, especially useful in an emergency.

- Stay calm and in control of situations. Reflect after the incident.

- Your first death on the ward is always a tough one. The sooner you experience this the better because it's going to happen.

- Do your very best with each patient, and give them privacy and their dignity.

I have witnessed so many students over the years literally go to pieces when they were deferred. There were times when I really felt for them, especially those who had come to the end of the academic road; informed that they now had to leave the programme. In some cases it was a loss to the service of a caring and conscientious person, simply because they could not hold it together for the duration of the examinations or assignments. They had also realised that they could not cope with the academic level of the programme. There was a lot of academic work required for each module, and yes it is important for students to access research to understand the theory behind the practice. When I was a nursing assistant on Kenwyn Ward, student nurses were taught on the wards. Their tutors would come onto the wards to undertake assessments whilst they practiced. Students also had periods of study in the school of nursing, but this was phased out years ago.

On the other hand, there were some students who would spend the entire three years literally horizontal, leaving everything to the last minute, assignments, portfolios, presentations, not getting out of bed to be on time for lectures. One of my closest friends who did just that received a distinction! It was strange to think that we were no longer the first year students, no longer on the bottom scale of the pecking order. In six months' time I would be a qualified nurse. Well, fingers crossed! I longed to graduate to what I believed to be the pinnacle of this profession. Halfway through my third year exams and passing them, I felt on top of the world. Not long to go now I would say to myself. Then reality hit me. This was just the foundation of the huge responsibility it would be to become a mental health nurse.

My efforts were finally rewarded by obtaining my RMN (Registered Mental Nurse) registration in September 2000. I didn't get a distinction, neither was I student of the year, but I did complete the programme and

I did get a good mark. I also gained a diploma in nursing. This triggered a flash in my head that if I ever bumped into any of my old school teachers, I could now tell them that I was a qualified nurse, despite being informed by most that I wasn't bright enough. I never did though. I graduated in Plymouth, Devon with most of my cohort. It was a day I will always remember. It was also a huge bonus to have my parents attending this special occasion. It certainly didn't do any harm to have them sitting in the audience at the Plymouth Pavilions grinning broadly and showing their appreciation of what had been achieved with the display of the thumbs up. My Dad held up a sign above his head saying, 'Are we still on for having window cake with our tea this afternoon?' The next sign that appeared seconds after said, 'You still owe me a tenner!' Mum didn't help either, her sign said, 'Have you heard of a new band called Coldplay?'

My parents had moved back to Vancouver when they retired and had flown in for a holiday. It was a lovely atmosphere and everyone was proud. I was standing there having my photograph taken (waiting for someone to pinch my cheek). Meanwhile, in the background one of the directors of the trust said to me, 'Paul, start knocking on everyone's doors, tell everyone who you are, why you are here, and what you can deliver.' Those words have never left me and really paid off. It's about getting your foot in the door. There were times when I would be disappointed and not achieve what I had been striving for, but I got over it.

Over the coming months there was some discussion about perhaps moving out of the county to gain further experience, but I decided that the upheaval of moving would be too much at the time. I wasted no time in applying for a staff nurse post on Loveny Ward (St Lawrence's Hospital) a psychiatric intensive care unit (PICU). I felt that I needed at least a year to consolidate what I had learnt; of course, the roles of healthcare assistant and staff nurse are completely different. I was now accountable for my practice. The year went so quickly and soon I started to feel comfortable in this new role.

In 2002 I was approached by more than one colleague and my career took an interesting and unexpected turn. 'Here Paul, have you seen this job advert? The Trust is looking for an NVQ co-ordinator for the county. This is you all over, and you're always supporting other healthcare assistants and students.' I looked and read the job description but said 'No'. I had not been long qualified and needed more time to consolidate what I had learnt. My colleagues didn't agree and this went on for a few weeks. People would say, 'Surely this is enough to whet your appetite?' The NVQ c0-ordinator post consisted of managing mental health NVQ candidates, assessing, teaching, inductions, assignment marking, and supporting candidates throughout their programme.

In the end, after a lot of thought and discussion I decided to apply. I thought that the interview process would be a good practice run; it would show people that I was interested in other areas. Indeed, it seemed like the right decision to try out different opportunities and I certainly felt so much more positive about the future. What I did have at this time was a variety of skills in my toolbox. I started digging around and doing my homework and finding out all I could about the advertisement. One thing I have learnt, is that it is not a good thing to fixate on the state of happiness or sadness of others based on where they may or may not be at the time. Why? Because all the time that you are looking left and right at the people around you and where they are at in their careers you're missing what's ahead of you.

I applied for the position, was short listed, attended the interview, and then fell off my chair. I was successful! It really was a 'You've got to be kidding' moment. It was a day that is tattooed on my mind. I was now the NVQ co-ordinator for mental health. This role was to be a new learning curve for me, and I did feel that I had a good sound knowledge of the various awards within the framework. My hopes and expectations of this post were that it would develop my teaching skills; I would attain a greater understanding about the teaching and assessing process. More than any other role, this felt like yet another new chapter in my career.

I remember thinking to myself 'I hope that I am successful and popular with the candidates, that I am judged as a good teacher and a fair assessor'. I was very aware by now that Cornwall was a large county, and I would be co-ordinating this myself. I was also aware that my predecessor had moved on to another post, leaving this one sitting vacant for some months. Alarm bells started to ring. I saw the county like a set of old fashioned scales, with me trying to balance them; getting one end running well, but the other end will start to tip if you're not around. I realised that at the time I had no idea of the scale of the whole process of managing it. Weeks into the post, finding my way around the office (not having seen a single candidate) I realised how unprepared I had been when I started. Although I had good knowledge of the mental health subjects that I was supposed to teach, I was unsure of the delivery, or how the teaching would take place. On reflection, it would have been a good idea to have made out a list of queries and met with my manager beforehand. By doing this I would have been less anxious about the first day.

I developed so much in this post as time went on. I started my D34 NVQ assessor award, and months later commenced the Certificate in Education (Cert Ed) which was for me one of the best courses I had completed. It took me two years and I got so much out of it; it was paramount to the job I was doing. At that time, it was a privilege to be up there in a classroom teaching the candidates the essential core modules of the vocational awards. I would often stop and think that my Dad was in a similar teaching role years ago. I know from others that he did it well and had a real skill for interacting with people. Following in my Dad's footsteps was never intentional and just happened. I'd come a long way since the roast potato incident and my shock announcement all those years ago! I had always said that I could never do the job that my Dad did, and here I was eerily mirroring what he had actually done himself. Today a high percentage of training is completed online (e-learning). Up for discussion? Bring it on!

The programme I was responsible for involved eight study days covering all the underpinning theory accompanying the training and assessment process. I would spend hours preparing these days which consisted of the principles of mental health, the experience of mental distress, effective communication, the working environment, and privacy and dignity. The teaching sessions would each last for four hours and would be delivered by myself and other professionals that I would bring on board. Eventually all the hard work and preparation would pay off.

As trainers we would assess each candidate to discover their own aspirations and the goals that they had set. I highlight the fact that different strategies were used for a number of reasons, thinking back to my Broadmoor days of learning. Candidates have a mixture of learning styles such as activist, reflector, theorist or pragmatist. Everyone is different, and we can learn in different ways. The management of this whole process was driven by me as the co-ordinator, along with two assessors. It had never occurred to me that teaching could be so tiring!

It wasn't just about teaching, but preparing lessons, booking rooms, sending out emails, marking assignments, mentoring, covering other trainers, and delivering mental health topics for their sessions. Another aspect of this role was being involved in the new cadet scheme and delivering presentations for open days for careers in health and social care. I also visited various schools around Cornwall to raise mental health awareness and the stigma that can be attached with students.

I have to say that I really enjoyed the teaching side of this role. Overcoming my initial nerves, I came to realise that it's a bit like being on stage. You can learn so much by observing other people teaching. Delivering a teaching session really gave me that sense of realisation that I could do it. I remember presenting a mental health awareness session to fifty odd police officers in the west of Cornwall, delivering them awareness of our services. I wasn't too sure how they would receive this as most officers and sergeants sat with their arms folded, rolling their eyes as if to say, 'What, another session to sit through?' As it happened I had some incredible feedback from this session, which really surprised me.

After I had finished my good forty-five-minute presentation and role play, I said thank you very much for listening to me, turned around to shut down the computer and what felt like an endless five minutes of silence turned into a round of applause. They had listened. I left an hour later after answering all their questions. Hours before delivering a presentation either at a meeting, conference or classroom setting I would go over what I would talk about. The danger point for me is if I start to read a newspaper before presenting, I might start to memorise headlines, and get side-tracked away from what I am about to deliver. Imagine spouting out the entire headlines of the front page of the Independent newspaper in front of a large audience. Right you are then!

You would quickly pick up the classroom vibes when teaching, conversations that went like this, 'I really do think that the best thing to do is for our group to take a vow that we just don't know.' In another corner would be, 'We must agree that none of us know about certain things more than others.' What they were actually saying, and what I have said myself in the past, is that we could learn together because we shouldn't have to feel stupid or be made to feel stupid about actually saying, 'We don't understand what you're talking about!' My task would be to put everyone in that classroom setting on an even level playing field.

Whilst undertaking the Certificate of Education and the D34 (internal NVQ Assessor Award) both hefty programmes, and along with my new role, I took on the Royal College of Nursing Clinical Leadership Programme. It was a year-long programme and another chapter in my career that really gave me so much focus within my job and my personal life. There was a structured focus, a theme throughout the course, on Stephen Covey and the seven habits of highly effective people. The programme and all those that attended with me would probably agree that a book could be written about this year in which we were all so inspired. Yet again, I felt privileged to meet so many new people who worked throughout the county, and became quite close to them during the course of the programme. Taking part in this programme was another one of the most exciting and pleasurable experiences of my career. Doing things that would normally not come my way within daily life.

You had to feel safe in disclosing issues to the core group. Group rules were drawn up and signed up to. This was the third course I had taken on in a year, running all three parallel. In those recent months I would be pulled in three directions at once. I would ping pong from one to the other trying to keep on top of it all. Suddenly my career path had gone stratospheric and the speed with which it was all happening was at times slightly difficult to handle. From week to week, day to day, and hour to hour, what with all the regular chores at home that came with raising the children, assignments, action learning sets, clinical work, presentations, meetings, tutorials, and very little sleep. I felt like one of those variety entertainers who spin plates on top of sticks, constantly rushing from one assignment to another, with just enough time to give one of the assignments the last final spin before it toppled over into my tutor's hands for marking. I would then be left with wide eyes, the loud ticking, and the countdown to the start of the next assignment.

I have to say I would come away buzzing and would set my action plans and have them all lined up within an hour. For me it was turning any negative issues into positive ones. It gave me so many ideas as an NVQ co-ordinator that I don't think the training department back then quite knew where I was coming from. But looking back there were no complaints. During this course we attended two days at Goodygrane, an old quarry in the west of Cornwall for team building exercises. I completed the Myers Briggs Indicator (Personality Inventory). We set up action learning sets, delivered presentations, and brought new ideas into our individual daily work places.

Our arranged visit to the House of Commons in London really fascinated me. The cohort was delighted that Candy Atherton Labour MP had obtained permits for all of us. Within the programme we visited supermarkets to make observations of people and their interactions whilst shopping. Action Learning Sets were a core part of this programme and have always stayed with me through my practice, a process of learning from past actions and results. It concerns both learning and doing. We would meet and work in groups to examine issues that we had. In the following months, members would start to reflect about all their concerns, considering issues that arose in their clinical workplace, and return to the groups to discuss how best to resolve them. Even now, as I look through my portfolio, I realise our leader would be proud that those learnt skills are still being used and it brings a tear to my eye.

I will never forget Stephen Covey's Habit 7: Sharpen the Saw. This was me all over at that time. Suppose you were to come upon someone in the woods working feverishly to saw down a tree. 'What are you doing?', you ask. 'Can't you see?' Comes the impatient reply. 'I'm sawing down this tree.' 'You look exhausted!', you exclaim. 'How long have you been at it?' 'Over five hours', he returns, 'and I'm beat! This is hard work.' 'Well why don't you take a break for a few minutes and sharpen that saw?', you enquire. 'I'm sure it would go a lot faster.' 'I don't have time to sharpen the saw', the man says emphatically, 'I'm far too busy sawing.' In 2012, I attended a further six month Leadership Programme in Newquay, Cornwall and felt proud that I still had those learnt qualities in place.

We had a brilliant lead for the Royal College of Nursing Clinical Leadership Programme. What was just awesome was the fact that he just made so much sense. He had a way of saying things and holding himself that was so together and so precise, yet he was completely unaware of how profound he was. He was always full of energy, loved the practical jokes, and possessed a sharp wit and a sparkling sense of humour. He would always support my visions and had the courage to enable me to roll them out. Clearly a leader who was accessible at all times.

At times I have felt that there were certain individuals who would criticise you for having a vision. This lead would always see the goods I had, and that I had the tools to do it, and at all times stand by me. Alongside this he had remarkable determination which drove his career forever onwards and upwards. By far one of the most dedicated people I have ever met.

Everyone in the cohort was asked to look for a mentor for the next twelve months. This person had to be someone who worked outside of the NHS, someone who had inspired us, and was a leader. I remember driving home thinking who on earth I could ask, a manager of a super market or HMV came to mind; it may have been because weeks prior to this we were in the supermarkets carrying out observations of people shopping. Observing how each person interacted, what they purchased, and why they had chosen that product. It wasn't until later on that evening that the penny dropped and I thought I know who this will be, the man I have always admired, Sir Richard Branson. Why wouldn't I with all that he has achieved: Virgin Record Shops, Virgin Record Label, Virgin Atlantic Airways, Virgin Rail, Virgin Publishing, there's more?

I thought it through for a few days and decided that if I asked him to mentor me once every two months, it would probably fit into his schedule. If I made my own way to his headquarters in London he may consider my request. With assistance, I penned a letter and photocopied highlights of my portfolio – all of which came to 200 pages! I wanted the letter to have a bit of clout when 'Sir' opened it and didn't want him to think 'Oh no, not another one.' I packaged it all up and sent it off special delivery.

Dear Sir Richard Branson,

Re – Nursing, Mentorship, Leadership, Vision.

At the youthful age of 40 I commenced my training to become a Registered Nurse in Mental Health. At that time I had spent 22 years working as a Nursing Assistant. Now some five years on I am an NVQ Co-ordinator in Mental Health responsible for training all Healthcare Assistants within Cornwall. I am looking for a mentor who will inspire, challenge, direct and enable a clearer vision in the roles I undertake and my aspirations for the future. If I were asked to put up a picture of someone who represented these qualities I would choose you. It is my belief that your success to date demonstrates a clear ability to motivate, inspire and lead your team in a positive and effective way.

I have recently commenced the Royal College of Nursing Clinical Leadership Programme, a programme designed to develop the leadership skills that we, as nurses, may hold but don't utilise effectively and also to assist us in developing new skills. The programme requires its participants to seek out a mentor, who preferably works outside our field.

Working in the NHS today full of grey–suited individuals, clipboards laden with tick boxes, targets and agendas for change, I perceive there to be a need for me to look beyond asking the usual recommended figureheads and for someone who I hold in high regard.

My requirements would be to meet with you no more than once every two months and for approximately a one hour appointment. I acknowledge that you are extremely busy but would be most appreciative, if this was achievable or if we could speak to discuss it further.

Yours sincerely,

Paul Deacon

I then waited in anticipation for a reply. I thought, if I could crack this one it would really be amazing what with all his knowledge of how to really get there, all the things he had achieved and completed. Every day the mail would arrive and I would check through looking for that Virgin letter. Three weeks later it arrived. Imagine my delight when I read his personally penned letter:

Reply:

Dear Paul,

Many thanks for your letter – I'm flattered!

Sadly I'm up to my eyes with current commitments so I simply cannot do justice to your request.

I'm really sorry to disappoint you but really wish you the very best of luck with your future challenges. You are doing well.

Kind regards,

Richard Branson

Chairman,

Virgin Group of Companies

But, I didn't just give up there. Years down the road I tried again. Sometimes it's difficult to explain such a moment. Just after writing this chapter I walked outside the door of my house on a warm summer's evening on Bodmin Moor. I could look across acres of woodland that dipped into a valley before rising again into the skyline. It was only split seconds later, and looking up at the sky I couldn't believe that precise moment seeing a Virgin Air Balloon flying over the blue Bodmin Moor sky. It was just awesome and ironic.

Chapter Eighteen

Guess Who's Arrived on the Ward

An opportunity arose when a charge nurse post was advertised for one of the acute inpatient admission wards. I applied for this post and was appointed. This would be my next learning curve. I have very fond memories of this ward and everyone was very forward thinking and grounded. There was a lot of experience amongst the staff; the ward reminded me of Woodstock Ward at Broadmoor Hospital, who also flew the flag high. Everything that came our way or we were asked to deliver on, including rolling out pilot schemes, we did it. The core of this work linked in with Essence of Care led by our lead nurse. It gave me two years' experience in this role which was so beneficial.

However, a year later we received the most devastating news that a team would ever want to hear. We were to close as a ward and amalgamate with our sister ward. It was a time when the ward had reached a very high peak. We had embraced so many national initiatives, including the Tidal Model and, most of all, Essence of Care to the maximum. The ward manager, nurse consultant, myself and others had to bring the philosophies of both wards together in order to work as an effective team. We were up against tight timescales, and had staff making up their minds as to whether to get on board or relocate to other areas. It was a very difficult time for all of us, and I have to say I learnt a great deal on the way. This was also the reality of being in this position.

As part of a three day visit to Cornwall, Sir Charles Perry, Director of National Institute for Mental Health England (NIMHE), spent a day at the hospital to see how volunteers and independent visitors helped to shape our services and engage with service users. I was asked and delighted to take him and his colleagues around the ward. At the time I was the charge nurse. His feedback was so inspiring to the team. We had just received the Trust's Team of the Year award, and were awaiting feedback from our AIMS-PICU Accreditation for Acute Inpatient Mental Health Services outcome (we received a Level One: Excellence). Weeks later I received a lovely letter and an invitation to be a key speaker at their annual conference in Torquay, which I accepted and attended six weeks later. It was such a brilliant experience, the fact that I was given a stage to speak about all the positive work that we were doing on the admission and Psychiatric Intensive Care Unit (PICU) and how this had made such a difference to all the patients that had been admitted to us.

I was the on-call manager one Sunday and based myself on the acute admission ward; I was still the charge nurse at the time. It was a very busy day and the team were flat out. I found myself out on the floor giving the team a hand. Around 4pm I decided that we all needed a tray of tea so off I went to the kitchen. On route the doorbell rang and off I went to answer it. As I approached the door I looked twice, standing there was Martin Clunes. I watched very little television apart from the news and documentaries (not forgetting any music programmes) but I have to say that *Doc Martin* had me glued, and I became a real fan of the series. I opened the door and was greeted by the man himself. I said 'mind your head' as he came in. I made this comment having seen him on numerous occasions entering his surgery office in the series and whacking his head!

Martin shook my hand and informed me he had come to visit a friend of his who was residing on the ward. We had a conversation (led by him) all about his past filming at St Lawrence's years gone, I took him verbally through the areas of the hospital radial block with Cober, Camel and St German's wards. After about twenty minutes I took him onto the unit. He was really interested in the history of the hospital (the old St Lawrence's). It felt strange seeing him on the next series of *Doc Martin*. One minute he was on our ward, the next he was back in his surgery. The following morning, I was brushing my teeth thinking, 'Yes Paul you were right', it would have been a real conflict of interest to be requesting Mr Clunes autograph. Driving into work I thought ah, he signed in before coming onto the ward. Months later Martin Clunes opened a podcast for our lead nurse entitled 'Depression'. In 2012 I met Caroline Catz who played Doc Martin's partner Louisa in the series and watched them shoot their scenes in Port Isaac. They seemed to fit in really well with the locals as if they were all one big family. During my working career, I would go on to meet government cabinet ministers, Robson Green, Tim Smit, Terry Waite, Ruby Wax and Billy Bragg.

One particularly exciting project arose in 2009. Our lead nurse at the hospital approached me to discuss compiling a podcast on 'What is a psychiatric intensive care unit?' I jumped at this idea as it was an opportunity to get numerous professionals, carers, patients etc. all saying their bit, and getting a message out to people as to what we did. It can be very daunting for patients coming into a PICU and not knowing anything about the unit. We approached two patients, the pharmacist, consultant, staff nurse, healthcare assistants, Mental Health Act adviser, holistic therapist and the activity co-ordinator to participate in recording the first podcast. This was then edited and we felt really pleased with the end result. We gave many copies away at a NAPICU (National Association of Psychiatric Intensive Care and Low Secure Units) conference where we had a ward stand to showcase best practice for our colleagues.

The lead nurse and I were involved in many new projects over the year. Some of the early NVQ projects we implemented were very focused on the candidates who were striving to complete their award. There are certain people that you can work with throughout your career who were just absolutely brilliant. It would be incredibly hard work rolling out new projects but very rewarding. It was extremely challenging, fulfilling, and at times difficult. You would start with the basics and over months watch it grow. The conversation would quite often be 'That's very good, that piece was excellent so keep that bit, but maybe we could get rid of this bit and try this instead.'

There are people who work in mental health at a national level who I have learnt so much from. There are far too many to mention here by name. For all their accolades and awards they are still in touch with the real world. Having seen it, done it and written the books (literally) they still couldn't have been more focused, approachable and encouraging to others. You'd never feel uncomfortable in their presence. It wouldn't matter if you were the waiter, a road sweeper, serving tea in the canteen or working in a hotel, you are a person and you would be listened too. Working alongside people with this chemistry would make you both equally determined not to let it slide into being just another great idea that never went anywhere. It was all about keeping it live.

It also made me determined that I was not going to be one of those people who just did the same old thing over and over. For every new initiative, nursing staff would meet up, get the coffee on and one of you would pull out your laptop, someone else would sit and type whilst another one would pace around talking their thoughts aloud and trying to capture the project. Most of the time we would be onto a winner and would get down to work and have a draft laid out to what we wanted to achieve. We learnt from experience and there was always a glimmer of hope that this new piece of work would be a real possibility.

The content would start to flow. After many hours work, we'd eventually feel exhausted, but felt quite confident that we had written a good piece of work. Even with all our enthusiasm, there were times where none of us would get around to actually putting anything down on paper. What we did achieve would then be presented to the trust board meetings, and we would leave feeling elated. Our lead nurse was such a phenomenal nurse that everyone who worked with him just wanted to deliver more. Throughout my years I have been so in awe some of the people I have worked with that I sometimes found it hard to deliver my best work. This went back to my early Pat Broderick days working on Kenwyn Ward when I was so desperate not to mess things up, that it would fully occupy my mind and I'd find myself second guessing my instincts and would start to question myself.

In 2009, I was on the admission ward undertaking an audit with one of the directors. Half way through this audit I received a telephone call from our deputy chief executive asking what I was doing at the moment. When I told him about the audit, he asked me to rearrange it for another day and to meet him on another ward. I felt a bit uncomfortable saying to this director, but they were fine with it so I made my way down the corridor wondering what all this was about. When I got there, I was met by the deputy chief executive and a fellow charge nurse. He explained that Camilla Parker Bowles (the Duchess of Cornwall) would be visiting in the next ten days. He also informed me that the low secure unit charge nurse and I would be taking the Duchess around the unit and the healing garden, which joined onto the PICU. The Friends of Bodmin Hospital had donated money towards the garden and were fully involved with the visit.

We had several meetings to plan the visit, with the police and the staff who would be on duty that day. Our communication lead asked for a staff member working within the hospital to give permission for their child to hand Camilla a bouquet of flowers. My twin daughters undertook this role and they did a fantastic job presenting the flowers. On the date of her visit she arrived at the hospital and was greeted by our chief executive, The Friends of Bodmin Hospital, and my girls. Photos were taken on arrival, and she then made her way to the unit where we took her around the ward and the garden. The visit was very successful and her questions were answered.

Apart from the academic side of things, I was personally working towards, I became involved in the Tidal Model, Essence of Care, the Certificate in Community Mental Health, training, mentoring, the cadet scheme, delivering presentations to schools on mental health awareness, jointly compiling policies, and visiting Broadmoor Hospital with staff nurses, nursing assistants and student nurses.

Chapter Nineteen

What Seemed Impossible Now Becomes Attainable and Ordinary

In 2007 I was appointed ward manager of a PICU, a 15-bed mixed ward sited within Cornwall. I had finally got there. The long pathway of my journey and all the snakes and ladders, the walls and bridges, the obstacles and solutions that I had gone through over the years. This particular day still sticks in my mind because of the outcome that I achieved. All my questioning and self-doubt about my abilities for the first twenty years. It made me reflect on those including myself whose education didn't follow the conventional path, and how good it is to see others succeed especially when the odds are stacked against you.

You don't have to be held back by your past. There are plenty of second chances for people to qualify outside of the usual school system. This post was also to bring the most important opportunity so far. I remained in this position for four years. The ward opened in August 2002. We as a team had won the NAPICU Team of the Year award twice (2004 and 2008). The award, hosted by NAPICU, recognised excellence within PICU services in terms of the care provided, team working and service improvement.

We also achieved a Level One (Excellence) in the Royal College of Psychiatry AIMS-PICU Accreditation; being one of the first PICUs nationally to become accredited. We had worked so hard over the year to work through 268 odd standards, to demonstrate evidence of best practice and that we were maintaining high standards. We worked at such a pace. Right from the beginning, everyone had been given a complete schedule for the whole process. As a team, we were absolutely focused on getting it right, and it made you feel proud. The worst time was waiting for the feedback of the results of the accreditation. We were informed at the time that it could be up to three months before we would hear anything. So we waited and waited, and the day finally came. I guess, with hindsight, all of us were preparing for the big review day to come, and I have to say under the circumstances we did really well.

Press coverage read: 'Excellent Psychiatric Intensive Care' and that our PICU was the first of its kind in the South West and one of only three units in the UK to be rated as 'Excellent' by the Royal College of Psychiatrists in England and Wales. The PICU achieved the highest possible rating after an extensive peer review.

This was a very exciting time for us all in the team. A tremendous sense of camaraderie builds up within the team when they are preparing for a challenge. This was our challenge. The Accreditation of Inpatient Mental Health Services (AIMS) is an initiative from the Royal College of Psychiatrists Centre for Quality Improvement. It identifies and acknowledges services that have maintained high standards of patient care based on a review of recognised best practice. AIMs initially included working age adult units and later expanded to psychiatric intensive care units, older people's units, and rehabilitation units. The main purpose of AIMs is to improve the quality of care in inpatient mental health units, and to acknowledge services which have maintained high standards of patient care. Each branch of AIMs has a set of best practice standards and these are used in all stages of the review process.

The standards are developed from key documents, requirements and recommendations set out nationally, and with input from key stakeholders, service users, carers, commissioners and regulators of the quality of the service being provided. From the time the service registers with AIMs, it can take six to nine months for them to gain accreditation. In order to gain accreditation, three main stages need to be completed: a self-review, peer review, and the final decision stage.

For the self-review, the service is required to complete a ward manager questionnaire, a checklist of policies and procedures, an environment and facilities audit, and audit of patients notes, distribute questionnaires to staff, patients and carers, and ensure that they meet the return targets for each questionnaire.

To complete the self-review the multidisciplinary team comes together to review their local procedures and practices against the standards and, if necessary, start implementing the changes required to achieve the accreditation. The service has three months to complete their self-review. The AIMs team then compiles this information into a workbook which forms the base of the discussion at the peer-review visit.

The peer-review by an external team takes place four to eight weeks after the self-review has been completed. A team, generally of four people and comprising staff from other member services and a service user and/ or carer representative, will undertake a peer-review visit. In addition to validating your self-review, the peer-review provides an opportunity for discussion, sharing of ideas and for the visiting team to offer advice and support.

Finally, the accreditation decision. Information from the self and peer reviews is compiled into a summary report which is verified by the lead reviewer and the service before being submitted to the Accreditation Committee. The Committee makes a recommendation about the service's accreditation to the Special Committee on Professional Practice and Ethics (SCPPE), as the awarding body. The unit will either be accredited, have accreditation deferred or not be accredited.

Everyone in the team had really good ideas which were valued and encouraged. For me as a manager it was about enabling the team to ensure any changes and best practice were implemented. I wanted to further the ward's horizon. The emphasis being to ensure that the quality of care delivered to the patient was of the highest standard. I would make a list of any ideas I had and keep it updated. I would stick them up on the wall, sometimes even using pictures: this is what our goal is, or this is what we are working towards. This helped us all to achieve these things, to visualise and inspire. In 2008, Dr Nick Kitson RC (Responsible Clinician) and the team were highly commended Psychiatry Team of the Year in the annual Hospital Doctor Awards. Dr Kitson had a wealth of experience working in mental health.

During my time on the ward, one of the things that stood out for me was at how difficult it could be to release staff for training. My thoughts turned to bringing these training sessions onto the PICU. The same week that I had this idea, I got together with our lead nurse and we compiled weekly training sessions. It gave our team and neighbouring teams the opportunity to refresh their skills and update themselves on best practice and legislation. We compiled a six week programme that people could see in advance.

The idea of in-house training seemed the obvious solution and the way we tailored it was to provide people with exactly what they wanted. If someone requested a specific topic then that is what they would get. My previous role in the training department really assisted me, knowing who to contact to get either internal or external speakers onto the PICU. We discovered that all those who attended the training really appreciated this opportunity. My observation was that it also brought staff together to once again share best practice and to network, and of course it also brought people through the PICU doors, so that we could demonstrate what we did on a day to day basis. Months later I became the ward's teaching representative. It really made sense having just returned to practice, and with all the educational knowledge I had learnt over time.

The team had also been selected as finalists in the Innovative Acute Care Category for the 2009 South West Health and Social Care Awards. John Sergeant was the Master of Ceremony for the evening. A very funny and tuned in person. Our entry had been chosen out of hundreds of applications that had been received as being a very good example of best practice. The letter stated that as finalists we had been invited to the prestigious awards ceremony which was to be held at the Westland Conference Centre in Yeovil on May 7th 2009.

Two weeks later I was out of the county attending a national conference when we received a call to say that the film crew assigned to the Health and Social Care awards ceremony wanted to come down to the ward and shoot some coverage for the evening's awards. Our lead nurse kindly stepped in and took the crew around, and was also asked to do a commentary. When we arrived at the awards ceremony we were given champagne and asked to stand by our show case. We had a professional write up in the ceremony programme, which also stated that from an impressive 337 entries in the South West Region, 40 of those applications made it all the way to a finalist nomination on the night.

On entering the main arena, it looked just like the Britt Awards, very nice indeed. Everyone was exchanging pleasantries. The mood was set, everyone was determined to enjoy every minute of the evening. We were right smack dab in the middle of the venue. I mingled with people who were lively, bright and excited about what was going on around them. After the grand three course meal there was an introduction by NHS South West Chairman, Sir Michael Pitt. It was impressive when our turn came and we viewed the footage that was screened on three gigantic screens across the venue, this was now our ward! We came third in our category, but believe me we were really pleased that we had even got to this stage. The whole evening was filmed, and we managed to get a copy of the entire evening on DVD.

I started to hear about NAPICU in 2004 when I returned to practice from the Education and Training Department. In fact on my first day back on the PICU I was invited to what was called a NAPICU Quarterly Meeting, that our ward was hosting, in Newquay, Cornwall. I went along to the day and have to say I was really taken back with what was delivered by the team and all the external speakers. It was a day of listening to presentations, sharing best practice, networking, and meeting people who also worked in PICUs around the country.

It wasn't long before I attended the annual NAPICU conference in Lancashire with other ward team members. It was a two-day event and this was when it all fell into place. I thought the quarterly meetings were inspiring; but the conferences were amazing. We were privileged to hear some of the nation's top speakers delivering topics around psychiatric intensive care units and low secure units. There were various stalls set up around the site where trusts advertised themselves and their projects, and were on hand to discuss information with you. I remember driving back home with others from the ward thinking what a brilliant job NAPICU had done. I continued to attend quarterly meetings around the country and attended as many conferences as I could. For myself, this was all about networking and sharing best practice, and I knew this was for me.

There are times I have had the sense of being in the right place at the right time. It's also about knowing and networking with the right people. If you think about it, the more you're out there and working, the more people you are going to meet. This is where you will find your opportunities.

The unit was going through some very exciting times which motivated the team to move things on. We won the NAPICU Team of The Year Award, and the poster competition for which we had compiled posters with details of all the initiatives we were introducing to the ward. Our ward consultant, Dr Kitson, felt that I should be more involved in NAPICU and that I should sign up to attend the executive meetings as an observer, to see if I could get more involved. I think what he was trying to say was that I had too much energy and needed to burn it off! Dr Kitson would often look at me not knowing quite what was coming next; you could just see the bubble above his head thinking 'Right, fasten your seat belt!' I have to say I was really up for this and wasted no time in feeding back that this was something that I really would like to do.

It wasn't until months later that Dr Kitson approached me on the ward. I will never forget the day when he was hovering around by my office door and asked if we could have a chat. I wasn't quite sure what was coming, well you never know, and straightened myself up in the chair. I was wondering if it had anything to do with all the meetings that we had attended (we had so many of them) and that he was going to apologise for kicking my ankles under the table when I wasn't supposed to discuss something. There were times that they would really swell up. (This was to become another method of communication in later meetings to come.)

Dr Kitson had written to Stephen Pereira, the Chairman of NAPICU, asking if he would consider allowing me to attend a meeting in the future. Weeks later a reply came back and I was invited as an observer of the Executive Committee. I attended six meetings which took place in London and Northampton. I found all of them really interesting, particularly as I was in the core forefront of a PICU. It certainly kept me up to date about what was happening nationally, and energised me on a day to day basis on the unit. As the months went by I became a regular participant and grabbed the opportunity to organise a quarterly meeting in Cornwall. This happened in 2011 when I organised our meeting at the The Alverton, a Grade II listed hotel in Truro.

The Alverton certainly had a high class feel to it, with so much character, set in the heart of the beautiful Cathedral City of Truro. The management team working at the hotel were extremely helpful, as were the Northern Networking team working for NAPICU. I really enjoyed all the co-ordinating and wanted this event to run smoothly. I also requested to chair the meeting. The day was set with various professionals delivering presentations about mental health. I wanted to provide a well thought out programme and feel that this did happen. The theme title for the Cornwall Quarterly Meeting was 'A Taste of Cornwall'. Feedback was that all the hard work had paid off and that it had been a really successful day with a hundred plus delegates attending including ex-colleagues from Broadmoor Hospital.

Months later I was nominated and appointed to the position of Deputy Director of Scientific Programmes. This was a huge boost to my career. I felt totally dedicated and active in what NAPICU do and how they deliver it. The PICU team and I also felt proud rolling out the pilot for the AIMS-PICU accreditation programme, and co-writing an article for the *Journal of Psychiatric Intensive Care* about our experience with AIMS-PICU. This also allowed me to present and deliver workshops seven times at the annual national conference, about our AIMS journey, step by step. Travelling back to Cornwall from the annual conferences and the executive meetings, I felt that I had all this up to date information in my head, like a conveyor belt with all the knowledge that I had absorbed over a two day period.

NAPICU is a rapidly expanding organisation committed to developing and promoting the intensive care speciality. The Association was officially formed in 1998 although the roots of its formation lie three years previous to that. The aims of NAPICU are to improve service user experience outcome and to promote staff support and development with psychiatric intensive care units and low secure units in a multidisciplinary manner.

Improving mechanisms of the delivery of psychiatric intensive care and low secure care, auditing effectiveness, promoting research, and education–practice development.

The Association uses a number of tools and methods to meet these aims, including quarterly meetings, academic seminars, e-newsletters, training initiatives, website, and of course the annual national conference. Various committees have been established to take an overview and further develop PICUs and LSUs through research, audit, training and education. A strategy and planning group is currently assembled, and this group works on gathering evidence-based data through a national audit to help formulate policy and influence the provision of high quality care in PICUs and LSUs.

In 2011 I was part of the AIMS-PICU review team for Isis Psychiatric Intensive Care Unit at Broadmoor Hospital. Having not long gained our Level One (Excellence) certificate, I started to branch out and do national AIMS reviews. I was part of the review team that went into Broadmoor Hospital, and spent an entire day reviewing their standards. It was a productive day, and the team had worked so hard to achieve these standards. When the team gathered to receive our end of the day feedback I was delighted to see all my ex-managers, directors and colleagues, which made me think of the journey that I had travelled.

Years ago, I had been their nursing assistant and healthcare assistant; these were some of the people who had supported me in my years working at Broadmoor. When I thanked them all again for the support they had given me they wouldn't hear any of it, and relayed that at the end of the day it was I who had the determination, drive, focus, that was required. As you can imagine once the day was over we all caught up with the news, and shared where we were all at. I left to travel back to Cornwall deep in thought about my time working there, and felt a flicker of excitement that I had previously experienced working with these fantastic teams. Weeks later I was involved in the co-ordination of a NAPICU quarterly meeting to be held in Wokingham, Berkshire. This was organised by Broadmoor Hospital (West London Mental Health NHS Trust). It was a superb quarterly meeting at which the ward manager and colleagues from Broadmoor delivered powerful presentations. I just had to get up and speak for five minutes, to inform the audience what an inspiring team they were.

Chapter Twenty

It Could Help

My own experiences in nursing have taught me that when you feel that you need to make changes, you need to decide what you want to do within your career and what you want to happen. Although this can be a daunting thought at first, you need to identify your long term goals. A career plan is a good starting point: where do you want to be in the next two to three years? What experience do you actually need, and do you have to gain qualifications to get there? Is there another area of nursing that you might want to specialise in apart from what you are working in at this present time? Is there a possibility of a secondment to another ward? My experience of moving to different areas is that this might mean a drop in salary and working conditions. If you don't take this, there is every chance that you will not get to where you wanted to be. I personally looked at it as an investment in my future. It enabled me to move from healthcare assistant to lead healthcare assistant, staff nurse, liaison nurse, charge nurse and then ward manager. All these moves enabled me to use my skills to develop myself and get to where I wanted to be.

Once your career plan is written, either in line management supervision or with someone in a position to guide you, then it becomes clear in your head. This will no doubt include some training courses. As I've said throughout this book, don't become paralysed at the thought of entering a classroom setting again if you were like me and your schooling days were not the best experience. I found it much more interesting to study subjects which related to what I was doing. It provides theory and practice, which are both paramount, under the one roof. As I have echoed throughout, nothing is going to come your way and fall into your lap, you need to stay proactive and go out there and grab it.

I also feel that going along and introducing myself to other professionals has helped me to build relationships and gained support. I have been signposted to the right areas and right people. This is something I cannot stress enough. For some that might be difficult, but it will get easier. There will be disappointments and you may not get the result you want, but people will know that you are interested. They will put a name to your face and you'll go onto the radar system for the future. I remember attending my Broadmoor interview and telling the panel who I was, and why I was the right person for this post, with all the years' experience I had gained working at St Lawrence's Hospital and the Monklands Hospital. To me it felt right that my drive, energy and the correct attitude were all desirable qualities, and they should offer me the post. It was also about the weeks of preparation before the interview, which enhanced my chances of gaining the post.

Pre-empting questions, talking about strengths and weaknesses, dedication and past hard work. Take your portfolio along for evidence, do some reading around the area of work, make an appointment to visit the ward if you are short listed, listen before you answer, don't have a pocket full of loose change, turn off your mobile phone, always make eye contact. Clarify any questions you're not sure of, go over your presentation, don't read every word of your power point presentation slides, and don't put too much information on each slide. Sort out what you are going to wear that day, how to get there, and make sure you have a drink of water first! Eventually all this hard work will pay off, but you do require the self-belief to know that you can achieve it. I know I may seem to go on about this, but this is how it was for me.

Once you have secured a post and have been there for two or three years you may start to feel stagnant, and that you are no longer learning. This is the time to move on. There is a the danger point when you are in your comfort zone and it can be difficult to break the cycle and bring about change. Throughout the course of your life change will occur no matter what. No matter how you plan or resist it, it will occur in ways that you can never have anticipated.

Chapter Twenty-One

Retiring

I have always said to myself that I hope I will have enough sense to retire when the time comes. Will I be able to walk away from this line of work when that time comes? How will I know when it has? You have to deliver in what you are trained in, and still have a life outside of it. Nobody really knows what's going to work until they have tried it. Life isn't always about living within your comfort zone.

The decision to retire and move on wasn't the difficult bit. It was which direction to take that posed the problems. I guess it's not too complicated to look back now and say what I could have, and should have done, as far as learning was concerned. Perhaps more importantly, I might have appreciated that such a remarkable opportunity was made available to me; but didn't take advantage of it. Or was it during all this foolishness and mayhem that all my basic thinking was suspended? Who knows. What would I have done for an occupation if I had not become a nurse? Perhaps I didn't realise it at the time, but at the age of sixteen I had the potential to do something with my life. Deep down I knew it, fell for it, and eventually did it. I was definitely ready for something. Nursing happened in the most amazing way because it wasn't anything I was looking for. In the beginning, it was a dream that slipped down the back of the sofa, along with the loose change from my trouser pockets.

At the end of the day, I reflected and learnt a lot from the various experiences I have had. It gave me a very good lesson on the flipside of being in different nursing roles. Some people may have given up in the first round; I hope not and if you think you have then stay focused. For all those out there who have said, 'I cannot do this', the reality is that you can, and I was one of those that did. Don't fold when the going gets tough. When you believe in something you can make it happen. It will give you hope, energy and motivation. If you were to keep saying to yourself that you won't or can't make something happen, you most probably won't make it happen. So what do you do? Sit within your four square walls? Take it easy? Do nothing? Or do you go for it? Once you have surrendered those chains you are off. To embark on your vision you have to have a baseline of self-belief in order to put yourself there in the first place. I am fully aware that some people can be tormented with self-doubt.

So much time is spent worrying when in all honesty no one knows what's coming around the corner. Don't let people put you out to pasture. There are times when you do need to stick your head above the parapet, and sometimes there will be someone out there who is ready to knock your block off. Even today, people's wings get clipped when instead they should be able to fly and flourish. People will say and do things all the time that might make you want to throw the towel in, but it's the people that stick it out, getting their heads down and persevering, that succeed. It's also all about the people you surround yourself with, because you can't do it alone.

I don't think I have been too disillusioned with aspects of my career. If you want to create something that you are proud of, it has to be fun and exercise your creative instincts. Every nurse goes through periods of great frustration, when you seriously question why you are pursuing what seems like an impossibly difficult profession. Nothing happens overnight. You have to work hard for years and years, because no kind of success is handed to you on a platter. My first unsuccessful attempts to do anything challenging have never deterred me. You have to be willing to push boundaries and take those risks, to be like a rubber ball that bounces back no matter how much life tries to get you down. On hearing that you weren't successful or not appointed in a job that you had applied for, your shoulders will sink, and a cloud of disappointment will descend on you. Other times will be the opposite and you will leap around punching the air! What will be, will be and that's the way of life.

I am so relieved that I'm still in touch with the old me, but on the other hand happy that my life has changed so much and for the better. Writing, whether it be a book, assignment or diary notes, can be a wonderful way of making sense of your life, and will remind you of all those fabulous memories. Even the most horrendous circumstances that one might encounter are part of the tool box that we create for ourselves and need to be reflected upon. As I said at the beginning of the book, my journey through life, both professionally and personally, has been challenging and overwhelming at times. The rewards were exceedingly great and have given me so much insight into the human condition.

Writing has allowed me to reflect deeply on my experiences over the last forty-one years and beyond; not least my colourful teenage years. I have to say that for me it was better to be born average and then work on myself. It makes you more determined to get there and to work so much harder. I have often been asked if I felt like I was on a treadmill. I guess that if I hadn't enjoyed my work and study then I might have said yes. It helps if you feel good about your role and that what you do is validated by colleagues. Developing further skills keeps everything fresh. I am fortunate enough to be able to say that there isn't one single appointed position that I turned down and later thought, why did I just do that?

No matter how prepared I was though, facing what I thought was the end of my career wasn't easy. It was yet another stomach-wrenching time, yet more closure. Not only was I departing from the PICU as a manager, I was now officially retiring. I now know that you shouldn't look at retirement as an ending, but a new beginning. We all spend too much time fretting about how the past is going to affect the future, and spend so too little time enjoying the present moment. 'What if' and 'if only' are redundant as far as I am concerned. There is no doubt that there was never what you may call a master plan, most of my growth has come about through passion and taking hold of life's opportunities with both hands. I do believe that everybody has opportunities of some sort. It's a question of whether you choose to take them or not.

The ward team and neighbouring teams had been through so much together that making the decision to retire was a difficult one. Every day I would walk through the airlock doors of my ward, and segments of my journey would flash before me. It took me back to the first day arriving at St Lawrence's, at Monkland's and at Broadmoor Hospital. My student nurse training, the NVQ co-ordinator role, all the courses and qualifications I had obtained. All the people I had met on the way. I began to feel for the first time how people must feel when they are made redundant or forced to retire. I was so used to going onto the wards on a daily basis that I was apprehensive that I would get real withdrawal symptoms about not being at work. I would miss not having something to do, people to talk to. I was lucky in some ways because I was employed and paid for doing a job that I loved and I managed to do so with very little compromise.

Life can be chaotic and chance plays a central role in everybody's life. Nobody knows how any decision you make is going to turn out. Elements of my career had been just taking the next available opportunity. Sometimes those opportunities didn't work out as I would of liked them to, but you don't know that when you reach out for that opportunity. A key moment in my career was making that decision to go and work at Broadmoor Hospital. Once I had made that decision I never regretted it, despite some pretty challenging and harrowing things that occurred whilst employed there.

Each part of my long journey was different and it made me think of all those skills I had learnt on the way. I walked into this field of nursing with an empty tool box, now I had several tool boxes and they were heavy. I had finally had a chance to make something of myself, at last I had been given an opportunity to achieve my goals and fulfil my potential. To me this is closure of forty-one years working in the centre of it all. I have never before felt so passionate about writing everything down. One reason for looking back over the past as far as my career was concerned, was to make use of experiences in making new and important decisions.

The evening of my retiring from the PICU ward and hospital finally arrived and I was really taken back when I was invited to 'my leaving bash' that had been organised by Maggie Atherton and colleagues. The evening took place in a venue that was all decked out with balloons, banners, a live band, disco, food and a personalised cake. I was presented with some lovely gifts, cards and two books containing messages from staff and patients. So much effort and time was put into the evening and believe me I was truly grateful. I was really pleased that Pat Broderick was there to deliver such a moving speech about all of us who had worked on his ward from 1977 onwards. It really did seem like the years had rolled back. I feel Pat needs to stand proud of all he has achieved. This man still maintains my admiration. We received written coverage and a photograph in our local Cornish Guardian of the evening events.

A part of me is still driven to try new adventures, to this day I still want to push myself to the limits. Having been through all of this and coming out of the other end still standing, I am very aware of how lucky I am. I have superb kids, family, friends, good health and have had the opportunity to work in a job which I loved so much. From day one I honestly didn't really think I stood much of a chance, but proved that it could be different and I loved the daily challenge. This continued wilfulness is the backbone of what I do. Banging away at those steel girder walls day and night with what at times feels like a blunt or broken chisel. At times I would tap into pure and utter misery, but this doesn't mean to say that I didn't have those magical spells of sunshine in the garden.

For sure I'm not suggesting that life is perfect now, but I know I have been very lucky. One of the things that I learnt very early on was that you get out of life what you put in. I remain proud that I still cling so hard to that working-class ethic that I came from, why wouldn't I? Thinking about it now, I probably did have a subconscious determination, an appetite to create new networks with people where I could demonstrate what I could do and express myself. There also seems to be a recurring theme. I appear to be one of those individuals right at the heart of things when a new adventure-initiative begins. People have asked me if writing this book has changed anything in me. I think it has. It has allowed me to look at life events from the outside; I have seen clear patterns that I had not been aware of previously. There are a lot of things in my past that I would not change if I could, simply because I would not be who I am now if I had not had those experiences. Everything in my diverse career pathway served a significant purpose throughout these years.

Waking up on the first day after retiring, it suddenly dawned on me that I was not holding a pile of paper work, answering phone calls, emails, faxes and documents which needed reading, signing and making decisions on. At work, everybody had a scheduled diary and all managers and senior staff needed to be in four places at the same time. Sometimes your schedule would tie in, but not often. There were times in my career when I felt like the luckiest person alive, but rarely shared this, knowing full well that there was always something coming round the corner. In the latter years this was more likely to be negative than positive. I am still eager to fill any idle moments with something interesting to do. I prefer to be doing something all the time and gain a lot of satisfaction from completing a job. There is something to be said about standing back after fulfilling a task and thinking 'Wow!' I do get moments when I am more than happy to just sit quietly and take everything in. Who knows, just because a person can do one thing is that all they should do for the rest of their career?

Summing up all those years working in mental health reveals that you cannot please all of the people all of the time. I sincerely gave it my best. Yesterday is history, tomorrow is a mystery and today is a gift. In 2012 I worked in a world where it seemed a sin to be tired. So, am I left with any regrets? Absolutely not, regrets are futile and a waste of energy. I truly believe that if you spend your time on regret, you serve nobody anything. Be thankful for what you have learnt and what you have achieved today, because it might not be there tomorrow. I have a rule that I don't look back. If I have made a decision, then so be it and I stick with it. So many people can relate to the fact that when a chapter of your life is closed, then it's closed. There is no room for time spent wishing things were different. Time is too precious to waste and there is too much to do and so much to see. Here today, gone tomorrow, just like those top ten hits. No matter what comes your way in life, you still have to deal and crack on with it.

So where am I today?

There isn't any kind of template for retiring, and I haven't found any instructions to follow. Sometimes when you think that you have finished, it turns out that really you haven't. After retiring and ploughing back into writing this book, I remain an active member for the NAPICU executive committee, as an NAPICU-AIMS lead. I continue doing national honorary AIMS lead reviews for PICU and low secure units for the Royal College of Psychiatrists. I have also started consultancy work at Broadmoor Hospital. I truly knew that I would not ever cut ties with this work arena and would find myself at least working part time. Being involved in all these different initiatives and programmes has taken me all over nationally. It's called networking and sharing best practice. From week to week, month to month, I travel all over the UK.

So much for retiring!

I am aware that at certain points in your life you come to a natural full stop and crave something new. On numerous occasions and totally out of the blue I have been approached by various people who were on the verge of launching new initiatives. There would always be a buzz of energy and excitement about them. They reminded me of myself in so many ways. More than once in my life, conversations have just gone in one ear and out the other (more so in 2012). But sometimes something would go in one ear, spin around twice and stay. I felt like I had been stung by more than one hornet. These people standing right in front of me had an aura about them which held my attention, sparking more than a bit of interest with me. It was their individual passion and vision to move things to a higher level within mental health. Some things in life have a strange way of tracking you down. Perhaps a suggestion that I was on the lookout for a new role? Or was there an observation around my detachment from being busy? It became more than a conversation and months down the road I would sign up; these new projects became priceless opportunities. This may sound odd, but my brain truly loves this type of challenge.

Believe me, the best leaders are the listeners who are visible, supportive and transparent. Listening to what was being said whether it be positive or negative, and acting on it immediately. There's nothing so exciting as being part of a group of such inspiring people who want to make that difference.

I continue to have best of both worlds career-wise. I love what I am doing at present and this also leaves me time to continue with all my commitments within mental health. What matters is not the choice, but that we are content with the choice. I am under no false illusions that one day all of this will come to an end when I will no longer be able to do all of this, it will be simply impossible. What I do feels like I have done for best part of my life. I have given so much to nursing, but it's also given so much back to me. For the time being though I am hanging on in there because I still have that energy. Nowhere on this planet do I feel more alive.

I do feel that I have balanced my time with my kids and work. They help me to stay young and focused. As for relaxing, well you will never guess what? I'm now a member of a local vinyl club! How brilliant is that? It's now 2019 and here I am again spinning that beautiful vinyl. I love the feeling when going home to place an album on my record deck. I spend hours reading the covers just like I used to do in those memorable 70s. I have missed this. The turntable, stylus, grooved album tracks, two sided recordings and the cardboard covers. It takes me back to the beginning of this story, with my brown paper bag hanging from my bike handle bars splitting under the weight of all the vinyl. Surely we all have a right to some sort of happiness? Embrace it and inhale it. I have also just returned from Vancouver having spent time there with my family. It was a real challenge trying to bring back the Canadian pressed Beatles' albums over in my suitcase. Albums in Canada remain very popular. My biggest fear was that I would be travelling back to London with my suitcase a lot heavier than when I came out. I could get hammered with a massive excess baggage charge.

So here we are, the final chapter of *Walls and Bridges*. Suddenly, it seems a very long time since I wrote the early chapters. Age does have a certain pattern of sneaking up on you in a way you thought it never would, goading you with long days of everlasting youth before one day walloping you in the face when you presumed to believe it would last forever. The reality is that nothing lasts forever. Everything has its good and bad points, and it is easy to look back on life with rose coloured glasses. However, I still can't help thinking that my youth, played out through the 70s, had many advantages over the modern day equivalent. As a family we were not rich, but we were most certainly rich in creativeness and imagination. Life was full on in a more laid-back way, you didn't have time to become frazzled or feel down. I can't help thinking that nowadays some of this magic has disappeared. The sense of freedom has expired, style has departed, creativity is absent. Laid back attitudes are not present, discipline and motivation is no more.

Time spent with the family is precious no matter what decade we grow up in. Quite often it was the little things that would build the best memories. Moments in between conversations that happened over mundane tasks, little things said and done would end up remaining in our memories as we grew older and now look back on. I learnt that nowadays we would spend a lot of time aspiring to do all the big things that would give us meaning and make us happy, but in the end it is the little things that always stand out. I would without a doubt, jump on a time machine in an instant, to relive those amazing days. I will always look back during these times with fond feelings of nostalgia.

To this day, I still love watching the BBC TV drama *Life on Mars* where they took a person from the 21st century and popped him right back into the 70s, the decade he grew up in. Transported back to the decade of flared trousers and glam rock, with its laddish 1973 Ford Cortinas and self-confident policemen.

I grew up at the right time, the right age, and in the right places. On reflection, I can truly say that the one negative of the 70s was discovering years down the road that appalling people such as Gary Glitter, Jimmy Savile and Rolf Harris, were all identified as abusers.

I hope that I have managed to give you an insight into my working world. It would be fabulous to think that maybe something positive can come from sharing this with you. I hope that this book will encourage others, if you have a vision and believe in it, then run with it. If you don't succeed, try, try and try again.

I have received accolades over the years, not least for being a stayer. A recognition that I am still in the same profession, I'm still at it, and if you're lucky you still have hair!

I haven't dropped the ball yet, and it's been more of a thrill than any other job has the right to be.

Chapter Twenty-Two

On the Front Line and the Lack of Support

I have worked with many ex-service people over the years. I have also been part of the hospital admission procedure admitting people with post-traumatic stress disorder (PTSD). Nursing people who have served in our armed forces and fought for our country has always left me feeling numb; there is no other word to describe it. The complete lack of support from the Ministry of Defence for soldiers who have been discharged, or left the services, or had to leave due to their injuries is appalling. Listening to their parents, their families and their experiences reveals a raw grief.

There were so many hospital admissions over the years, so many young men who were left to deal with the aftermath on their own. As a nurse, I was left feeling frustrated and inadequate, lacking the experience and training needed to gain a better understanding of what these people had been through. I would struggle with the fact that we were getting involved with other people's wars, when it costs so much money. We would hear on a weekly basis that our troops were underfunded and that they did not have the right equipment. Why send our troops away if we cannot support them? Surely the money could be spent on health rather than contributing to the loss of our soldiers' lives?

What follow are the words of a soldier who spent years on the front line in Iraq and Afghanistan. This person is a friend and I respect him immensely. Having been aware that I was writing this book about my journey I asked him if he wished to contribute by putting his side across. I am grateful that he agreed. I spent hours and hours in the late evenings and early mornings, listening to his journey. Very little of the content of his conversations ever had any happiness. I summed up his journey as grim, like so many others, until the end.

Please read on…

I now find myself a civilian after spending the last eleven years in the Army. Life for me now can be as turbulent as anyone's life can be. Anyone looking at me could see that I was normal, happy and fitted into the day to day trends of normal life. Like anyone else, my inner thoughts and past experiences would spin around in a sort of chaos way, and I would try to put these into some kind of order. This is the time that I had to fasten my seatbelt for the turbulence, as the ride could be bumpy.

I would be in the kitchen making a cup of tea one day and memories of a fun day at the beach will come into my mind, or a memory of a family meal where everyone would be laughing and having a nice time. Another day I'd be making a cup of tea and a painful memory of a broken relationship or the loss of a loved one would emerge leaving me feeling upset or unhappy. This is obviously a completely natural experience, to reminisce about past times, but what if you have experienced something horrific? Or perhaps something that felt unnatural? Those memories are harder to explain away.

Having spent eleven years in the Army I had those kinds of experiences, and the memories would stop me in my tracks. They would do the same to anyone. If such a memory would catch me unaware I would freeze for a few moments then everything else would fade away and I would find myself completely involved in this one thought, this one experience. Except, it would be more than just a memory because it would feel real, smell real, and sound real. In fact, it's as real as the words on this page. I would experience all the emotions that I felt at that time; I would be back in that horrific situation, and as quick as a flash I would be back in front of the kettle as if a hypnotist had said 'one, two, three, and you're back in the room'. The difference was that there would be a lasting effect of my memory; I'd be left agitated, it would be difficult to stop the thought from dominating the rest of my day.

These days it doesn't happen so much as I have been given the tools to deal with these kinds of situations. For example, if it does happen then I will say to myself out loud 'Stop!' and then think about my thought process and challenge it, and I will ask myself questions like 'what am I going to gain thinking about this?' Or 'if I carry on thinking about this, how is it going to make me feel?' If my conclusion is that things will not end well, then I will stop and distract myself, or go to the gym, or find other ways to take my mind off it. It could be as simple as thinking of the place where I was the happiest and having a nice time.

I know this may seem difficult to understand; the idea of a memory controlling behaviour, and if someone from the Army was to read this it is highly likely that they may be thinking exactly that, or perhaps that I'm being a little bit pathetic. There was a time when, if I was to have read the previous paragraph, I would have thrown the book in the bin muttering under my breath, 'what a looser, get a grip you pathetic individual.' However, these are the techniques I would later realise I needed to be responsible, healthy, and to lead a life without feeling angry at the world and destroying everything and everyone that I love, and in return loves me.

Two years ago, if anyone had asked me to write about my experience of Iraq and Afghanistan and how it would make me feel, I would more than likely have lost my temper, and just exploded into a fit of unreasonable aggression. Why would I have done that? As a boy I was kind, well mannered, and a bit of a mummy's boy with plans to join the Army and go to war because that is what the men in our family did. If it was the right thing for them then it would be the right thing for me, and this would make them all proud. And yes, it did make them proud. I was also proud of myself, and to this day I'm still proud of what I achieved and experienced. At the onset of my career in the Army everything was just great, I had gone off to train as a boy and returned a man, or so I thought. I look back now and I realise I was the man that the Army wanted me to be and the man I tried so hard to be, and somehow I lost myself. I lost my own thought process, and I feel this was my fault. I didn't want to be that 'mummy's boy' who couldn't read or play sports; I wanted to be a soldier. I wanted to be the guy that people respected and talked about in the pub. I got it and loved it.

I had completely given myself to the process of Army recruit training, and in return they had given me discipline, controlled aggression, an ethos of wanting to be the best in whatever I achieved. It gave me a feeling of belonging, and also an unquenchable thirst to go to war. That sensitive caring boy was now a distant memory and it was like he had never even walked this earth. I would just ignore any comments, as he would make me look weak in front of my work colleagues and I had spent too long feeling that way. Here I was at 17 years old, thinking I was unbreakable and hard as a coffin nail, ready to take on anything or anyone no matter what the consequences were. After training I settled into my unit, there was the obligatory ill treatment for being new and after a lot of hard work, and the odd slap, I finally became trusted as one of the lads.

By early January 2003 we were all glued to the television screens watching the tensions escalate between the USA and Iraq. My colleagues and I could almost smell the opportunity for a war and a chance to prove ourselves as soldiers. A few months later we found ourselves in Kuwait ready for our war on terror. I was primed, my mind was set, and my body was ready. We had all worked hard for this and the mixture of excitement and nervous tension was intoxicating, I really felt alive at that time.

A few nights before crossing the border we were told to write letters home in case the worst happened. I had heard all the intelligence briefs and our mission briefs, and this was the first time I had felt real fear; it was like someone dropping a boulder into the pit of my stomach. Maybe it was because I was actually writing down what *my family meant to me and the thought of never seeing them again was worrying to say the least. There was no amount of bravado that could take that feeling away. Maybe that feeling was the mummy's boy that I have tried so hard to ignore letting me know how I genuinely felt about the situation I was in. I didn't want to say anything to anyone, but I'm sure there were a lot of people feeling the same thing. No one said it, as it was not the 'done' thing to admit your fear. It would be an admission of weakness and we were not meant to be weak, so I just kept it to myself and tried to cover the feelings with a plaster of false confidence.*

A few days later the padre had prayed for us, the commanding officer had given his historic speech, and finally the Regimental Sergeant Major spoke, which was a very touching moment. We then loaded on to our transport, fully bombed up with ammunition and rations along with water. Two hours after setting off we crossed the border into our first war with a strange feeling, which to this day I cannot confidently label or identify. I can't work out if it was sheer terror or exhilaration, and even now I spend my time trying to figure out what it was.

By the end of June I was sitting in Basra airport ready to come home. I was only 18 years old, but I felt that I had aged ten years. Not because I had spent the last few months fighting, I felt aged because I had spent the last few months looking out into a desert and nothing much else. I had not proven myself as a soldier in any way; I was tired, angry and frustrated. There must have been 3000 guys in this mammoth hall and we were all waiting and talking about going home and what we would do when we finally got there. The excitement was overwhelming. It was a good feeling to have completed my first tour, even though it wasn't what I had wanted it to be.

Every now and again someone would pitch up and shout out names or flight details and other 'nif-naf', and then we were all instructed to be quiet and listen to the officer who banged on about if we felt stressed or if we drank too much, if we had got into trouble, or if we observed any of our friends having sudden changes in mood or being irrational, then to feed this back. I remember laughing to my friends about it and joking that this was our normal behaviour and what was this bloke on about? We all just shrugged it all off. It was only a five-minute brief; a form was then passed around and we all had to sign it. It was to say that we had received a brief informing us of the signs and symptoms of post-traumatic stress disorder (PTSD). This again gave us something else to have a good laugh about! PTSD? What a load of rubbish and where's our plane anyway because I'm sick of all this hanging around. [PTSD is the delayed re-experience of a psychological trauma. It is a result of an experience that the person found horrifying. They may have witnessed the atrocities of war, or a traumatic disaster, or experienced sexual or physical abuse.]

It was amazing coming home, I had never been away for so long and it was like an immense weight had been lifted off my shoulders. My family were over the moon to see me, and my friends were just as happy. We had parties and some good times. It wasn't long before silly questions where being asked, 'How many people did you kill'? 'Did you win the Victoria Cross?' I didn't know what to say. We did have a few fire fights but nothing of any significance at all, and in fact I felt like a fraud. Once everyone got used to me being back and settled, I started to slow down and unwind. This is when I found myself feeling irate over nothing at all, and just being very unhappy in a non-specific way.

I didn't know why if I was honest with myself, my war was really very quiet, there were some horrid situations, but for the most part of it, it was just boredom for months on end. On my return I found I was growing increasingly more frustrated and fed up all the time. When I drank alcohol I would flash into a fit of aggression and start to fight over any reason I could think of at the time. This would happen every time I was out socialising. There were no bad dreams or flashbacks, or any silliness from the brief we'd received at Basra airport; I was just dissatisfied that I didn't really fight any battles like I believed I would. I was frustrated that I had built myself up for the past few years wanting to go to war and when my chance came we had nothing.

I found this hard to get my head around and would find myself just constantly thinking about it, the thought of doing nothing in my so-called war really bothered me. Luckily enough I was then dragged into the Army boxing team. It felt a good way to get rid of all this built up aggression; it was cathartic. I knew at the time that there were lots of other guys feeling as disgruntled as me, but within months I felt good again so I just assumed they did as well and I thought nothing more about it.

After a few years Afghanistan had really started to heat up and I had a second chance to prove myself as a soldier. Once again I found myself writing letters to my family in case the worst happened. I had all the same mixed up emotions as before, but all I ever wanted was to go to war and over the next few years, with the back-to-back tours, I was going to get everything I had ever wanted. It was a busy time and I remember just getting on with it, working hard, doing the job I wanted to be doing. Throughout this time I ignored everything else; for me life was about operations then getting back and having a good time. It was a massively selfish and carefree time that I will actually always remember quite fondly. Maybe it was just my way of coping with the events unfolding at that time in my life, but that never dawned on me for a second.

We were always lucky that no one from my unit was ever killed or injured. Obviously it was happening around us but never too us. It was always a fantastic feeling of ecstasy coming back from a contact with the enemy unscathed having won the upper hand, which was then followed rapidly by exhaustion.

I'm certainly not saying I had the time of my life over there, some horrendous things happened, sometimes as a consequence of my/our actions, sometimes as a consequence of the Taliban's actions, but these things just didn't bother me much. It was just a part of life out there, it was what we trained for and it was by this time what we were used to.

When I eventually did arrive back home, it was great to meet up with my family and friends again, just as it had been before, but then it was back to camp for business as usual. Every now and again one of the lads would get drunk and become emotional about an event out on operations, but he would just be told to be quiet and it was put down to too much beer. Once when I was having a drink with a friend he mentioned to me about a medic who was rumoured to be 'losing it'. I knew that this guy was a fantastic medic and he had dealt with some horrific situations and had always done well, even when he had lost people. That was the nature of the beast. When I saw him in the pub he was always massively drunk, but this was the norm for blokes like us. Over the following months he just seemed to fall apart. He was caught cheating on his wife and every time I saw him in the pub he would be in complete disarray. People were talking about him, saying things about his mental health. I didn't know how to deal with him being such a mess in the pub, or at work so I just stayed away from him, as I didn't want to be dragged into his drama. Soon after he had disappeared to some training post out the way and that was the last I ever heard of him.

It was not long before it was time to be deployed back to Afghanistan. I said goodbye to everyone and before I knew it I was back out on patrol. Straight away this tour was different from the others, our lucky strike was finally over; one of the lads was killed by an IED (improvised explosive device) a week of being out there. That set the tone for the rest of the tour. It seemed we were encountering the enemy every time we went out on patrol and when we were not in contact with the Taliban we would find IEDs on almost a daily basis, even when we thought we were safe in our FOB (forward operating base) there would forever be attacks from mortar fire. It was truly relentless.

During this tour we lost a lot of the guys, mostly to IEDs. The lucky blokes would just be injured, but the injuries were never minor and always life changing. Sometimes I wondered whether those getting killed were actually the lucky ones. We were all good friends by this time and we all knew each other well. Despite the cliché, it really was just like a big family really. But when someone got killed or injured I would just carry on looking after the younger blokes. Everyone would put on a brave face, there wasn't time for grief or emotion, and we had a job to do. Regardless of what happened I would always go back out the next day to do the same thing and try not to hurt. Just like everyone else. I'm not saying that we did not mourn our friends because we did. Carrying a friend's coffin onto the back of an aircraft to be sent home to his wife or mother was the most emotional thing I have ever done, and *we would suffer. We would feel it, but mourning the loss of our friends, our brothers, that would have to come later for us.*

The tour was the longest and hardest I had ever done and it finally came to an end. I really felt relived it was over; I wasn't feeling bad about things that had happened. All I now wanted was to get back home. I would find myself thinking on the way back how amazing it was going to be walking in the front door with everyone there happy to see me, like it always had been in the past.

Before we arrived home, we had to spend the night in Cyprus on something called 'decompression'. This was 36 hours designed to let us blow off steam and calm down before going back to the UK. It involved entertainment, socialising, a few beers, and a chance to relax without thinking about the job. But this actually just annoyed me massively. It felt a waste of time, all I wanted was to be at home. We now had to spend the day on a beach, which after hanging around waiting for the RAF flight was bad news, all I wanted was to sleep. What we wanted was a little BBQ and a few beers, it was just so frustrating being locked up in a place no one wanted to be in. As well as this, we all had to attend a number of briefs about diseases we may have picked up over there, and also listen to a brief about the signs and symptoms of PTSD. We spent the time muttering about how much of a waste of time these briefs were, as no one really cared, and no one listened. The whole thing just felt like a covering exercise; empty and unconvincing.

Arriving back in the UK after six months away was a fantastic feeling. We spent a few days back in camp to get everything sorted and cleaned before going home on leave. On the morning before going home we held a remembrance service for the guys lost while on tour. It was a nice thing to do, as this was the first time we had all been together since leaving for Afghanistan. I knew that having a service was the only thing we could do to pay our respects but to me it just didn't feel enough, I felt like we should be doing more somehow. I could not get this feeling out of my mind; it was like there was a hole in the pit of my stomach that I could not get rid of. Arriving home later that evening it didn't feel like the amazing moment I had imagined for the last six months. Everyone was there and everyone was happy, but I just felt numb. I was going through the motions for everyone else's sake, I put it down to me being tired and just carried on.

Over the next few weeks everyone was making a fuss but I still didn't feel with it, if anything I felt anger. I was angry about my friends being killed and hurt. I was angry that they were still suffering in hospital. I was angry that I had spent the last six months of my life fighting in a war supposedly for the security of our country and I was surrounded by people who were more concerned about what clothes other people were wearing and who was winning the latest television talent contest. It didn't take long for me to start struggling with what felt like the monotonous grind of life back home. It felt like I was spending all my time just pretending. I was interested in what people had to say, but the honest truth was my mind was forever occupied with the last tour. Maybe I was trying to make sense of things which I just couldn't do.

I carried on like this for a while and everything seemed to be fine; no one noticed I was struggling, and for me that was good enough, but then I started to have trouble sleeping. I would wake up dripping with sweat because a second ago I was taking a huge rate of enemy fire and trying to get to my friend who was dealing with a casualty whilst the splash of the enemy fire was kicking the dirt up everywhere. Then I would be in complete darkness not knowing where I was or what was happening. I would be in a complete state of panic and it would take a few moments for me to realise that I was safe and that I was home in bed with my girlfriend who would be snoring blissfully on her side of the bed. I would then spend the next hour or so pacing the kitchen trying to relax and make sense of what had just happened. But the problem was I just couldn't relax. I couldn't wind down. I was always on edge and looking over my shoulder, and without sleep it was making everything worse.

The only way I could sleep soundly was to get drunk and then pass out. When I was drunk it felt like a break from being numb or irritated, but then a lot of the time I would just be angry and looking to take it out on anyone or anything. This meant that losing my temper and fighting started to become a regular occurrence, it felt good sometimes but then other times I was just a drunken, emotional, rambling mess and soon this started to have an effect on my relationships with friends and loved ones. Soon I became very isolated and insular. Even my work suffered through my utter lack of motivation. I just couldn't find it within myself to concentrate or apply myself to anything at all. The only guarantee was that I would be forever thinking about Afghanistan, not only the last tour, but also all the things that had happened in the past tours started to make an appearance. The truth of it was I was hurting and struggling to come to terms with my experiences and the loss of my friends and I just didn't know what to do with myself, it was like I was trapped and there was nowhere to hide, and no respite from my memories or the way I felt.

It was a Sunday morning and I was hung over at home staring at my cup of tea. My mother came in and begged me not to get angry and just to listen to her. Immediately I began to snap with her. Whether it was the beer from the night before or just the sheer lack of energy. I just sat there and listened. She must have spent two hours explaining to me what I had been doing and telling me what a state I was in, I sat there just waiting for her to say 'talk to me, you can tell me anything honestly you can'. But the fact is people say that with good intentions and they want to help, but how could I tell my own mother that after seeing a man get torn apart by an IED, with his blood and body parts still on me, the one thing I felt after picking myself up off the floor was sheer relief? How could I look someone in the eye and say that when I couldn't even look myself in the eye for shame?

As the conversation went on my mum pleaded with me to go and see the doctor back on camp and deep down I knew I was not well and something had to give. I also knew that going to see the doctor would expose me as being 'weak' and that this would be the end of my credibility. Most of my friends and colleagues would render me as untrustworthy or a malingerer looking for an easy way out. This filled me with utter fear. Being known as those things and being looked upon as unworthy felt like my world was closing in on me. Everything over the last eleven years that I had worked for could be taken away from me in the worst possible way. But I had some hard choices to make. I knew I couldn't go on like this for much longer; I could either carry on and ruin myself or risk my career.

That Sunday night before going back to work was the longest drive of my life, thinking about what to do. I remembered a conversation with a friend a few weeks before that I had forgotten about until that drive. It was simple, he said 'just let it go, your life will never be yours, and they're never going to stop sucking the life from you while you're still serving'. This made me feel greatly conflicted because I completely agreed with what he said, but felt like I was betraying the Army, my unit, my friends, even my family.

The following morning I told my boss that I needed to see the doctor because of a back injury. It was a horrid feeling having to lie to him but the thought of telling him the truth was too much to bear at that time. I was nervous enough, I didn't need to be worrying about him telling everyone and sniggering in the mess at my expense. I was booked in with the medical centre; it was a tri-service medical centre, which meant they looked after everyone at the barracks regardless of which branch of service you belonged to. Sitting in the waiting room for my appointment seemed to take an age but things always do when you're nervous. I still didn't know what I was going to say but soon enough I was sat in front of the doctor.

He looked on his computer and said 'I see you have a problem with your back' he just seemed indifferent as if he was just working at a checkout in a supermarket. I was so nervous I stuttered and said 'Well no, Sir', which didn't go down well at all. He snapped back 'Well what are you here for then?' This shocked me a little but I thought to myself 'bugger it just tell him'. So, I spent the next ten minutes explaining to him about the lack of sleep, nightmares, drinking, fighting, uncontrollable outbursts of rage and my lack of concentration, the ridiculous situations I had been getting into. I didn't stop for breath. When I finished the doctor just said, 'Well what is it you're here for? Is it lack of sleep?' I didn't know what to say. I just looked at him and said I didn't know what I needed. He tapped his fingers on the computer and then prescribed me four strong sleeping tablets and said to come back in two weeks if I still wasn't sleeping.

I was in shock, I didn't know what to expect when I went to the doctor, but I certainly wanted more than that. I was fuming and snapped at the lady handing out my sleeping tablets. I stormed out and bumped into my friend who was a medic for my company, the second I saw him I grabbed him by the scruff the neck. I don't know why I did this, but he soon pushed me off and asked me what was wrong, so I told him the whole story and I just broke down. I tried not to, it was the last thing I wanted people to see, but I just couldn't hold it back. I was giving in and admitting I was in pain. I was expecting him just to laugh and take the mick out of me but he didn't. He listened to me and then he said 'look, just go back to your room I will talk to our doctor as soon as I can.' I apologised to him and begged him not to say anything to the blokes. He told me to shut up and not to worry.

By the time I had driven back to my building the phone was ringing. The Army doctor from my unit wanted to meet right away and I was to go to his office. He sounded very concerned, and so with a sense of urgency I made my way over, this time without the nerves. By now I was enraged by the last doctor — how dare he just give me sleeping pills! That was not meant to happen. I didn't know what was actually meant to happen but not sleeping pills! I was going over the last appointment in my head walking up to the doctor's office. He was already outside the door waiting for me, he gestured me into his office and we walked in together. He closed the door and I sat down followed by the doctor, and he simply asked me what was going on and alluded to what had just happened back at the medical Centre.

So I spent the next hour going through my behaviour. I tried to explain the way that I felt about things, which was hard enough at the best of times, he started asking me questions about whether I thought I'd do something silly like hurt myself or take my own life or hurt someone else. I started to get flustered with this, but the doctor quickly jumped in and said he needed to know the answers to these questions because if there was a risk to myself or others then he would not be doing his job if he didn't find out, and that all he wanted to do was to help me and stop things escalating. I told him I didn't feel suicidal nor did I want to rampage through the camp killing everyone. I said I may feel like it sometimes but I wouldn't.

Then he just looked at me and said that he was glad that I came and saw him, he went on to say that he thought there was an epidemic of men on this camp suffering and that they would not come forward for fear of being ostracised or sneered at, which unfortunately would quite possibly happen. He assured me that this would stay between us and no one else would need to know. I was numb, I just didn't know what to say, the doctor had told me to inform anyone who asked that I had a slight back injury and needed rest, then I had to promise not to drink, and if I could feel myself getting worse or needed to talk to call him any time. He gave me his personal number. Just before I left, the doctor informed me that I was not the only one on the camp suffering. Out of everything that one statement felt like a massive weight off my shoulders.

Two weeks later a military psychologist was back in the medical department evaluating me. Just the simple act of sitting down and talking to someone and being heard made life seem a little easier. Throughout the evaluation he nodded his head and seemed to know what I was saying, he had a look of someone who was overworked and tired but he seemed like a nice bloke, he wanted to see me every week and I agreed as it felt like I had a small break every afternoon from the turmoil I was in. It felt good to be under someone's wing but having to go to him every week would be a problem as I would have to find an excuse every week to disappear for the afternoon, so I needed to talk to my platoon commander and tell him what had been going on and what I was up to. I was lucky as we got on well and he was an utter professional in every way. He told me to do whatever I needed to do, and then went on to say that it was like any other injury that needed time to heal. He promised me to give me cover and he kept his word because if the men had ever caught wind of it, it would have made life very hard.

So, for the next few months I would go and see my shrink and he would spend time prompting me, and then gave me exercises to do which helped to deal with things in a better way. At times it felt I wasn't getting anywhere but then I just kept going and slowly I started to lay some things to rest. I found writing a diary really helped me when trying to challenge my thought process. Viewing my thoughts on paper felt like I had given them some structure rather than just emotion. I was able to work through it and move on instead of dwelling on things too much. This combined with counselling and guidance I began to slow myself down or that's what it felt like and it gave me time to think about my actions and take some responsibility for myself. For example, not drinking to the point of losing my own self-control, and injecting self-discipline and gaining a routine for looking after myself better. All these things took a while but I was making positive steps, which was making me finally feel much better.

Life for me now can still be turbulent and not a day goes by when I don't think of my experiences from my time away, and yes I will still have the odd nightmare, but as I said in the beginning, I have gained the tools to deal with things properly. By this I mean in a healthy way and because of these tools and a note pad and pen, I don't worry so much. These things are still upsetting and I will still get emotional about it, but that's okay because that's natural. I don't think I will ever make sense of the situations I experienced over there and I have stopped trying to. I have let go of trying to find reasons for why things happen and just accept the hand that was dealt, and this way of thinking has worked so far.

I am now left wondering about the many other young men and women like me, who have been fighting wars since 2003. How many of the hundreds of thousands of them are struggling with their experiences? How many of them have been too scared to come forward? How many are suffering with PTSD now because they couldn't say anything.

There is obviously a system in place to help serving members of our armed forces. I'm a product of that, but I was a relatively simple case trying to deal with typical experiences associated with serving in the forces. There must be so many people so much worse off than me, but is there really enough support to go round for them within the MOD? What about all the people who have slipped through the net and are now out of the forces struggling with things, what's going to become of them? What if someone is suffering from PTSD and they are not in the forces anymore, can the NHS provide the resources to help these people? Is there enough experience to be able to relate to and understand what these sufferers are even talking about? Is there any support from the MOD for suffers of PTSD after they have left the forces or will it be left to an already overstretched NHS and limited charity groups? These are just a few of the questions I have now, and the most upsetting things are that I think everyone knows the answers to every single one.

I don't need a crystal ball to know that these hundreds, if not thousands, of ex-service men and women are struggling with their experiences from conflicts over the past ten years. They have probably now slipped into the civilian world and I know that if they go without help, or even a little guidance, their lives could fall apart in the worst possible way. After all they have been through, who is going to be there for them in their time of need?

I find myself now living as a civilian, which is a massive adjustment and a welcome one. I look back at my time served with a sense of privilege, I feel privileged to have experienced the worst side of humanity and also the best side. I'm extremely lucky to be sitting here right now while better men than me are no longer with us, and this is my greatest privilege to have known and served beside these men. Not a day goes by where I don't think of my friends, and I will have a quiet moment to myself and pay my respects as best as I can. It's my responsibility to live a happy and fulfilled life, I owe it to them as well as myself to be healthy, physically and mentally strong, and make the most of everything. So this is where I am today, happy, content and looking forward to the next chapter of my life.

Final words

In order to provide a visual impression and history of St Lawrence's Hospital, my brother compiled a website which has been running for a few years now (http://slhphotos.atspace.com/index.html). This contains the history of St Lawrence's Hospital, photographs, and events which give a better understanding of what it all looked like back then. It really is like going down memory lane for all those who worked there at the time. I am so much better working with visuals, and this site has also helped me to write this book.